Especially Father

By GLADYS TABER

ESPECIALLY SPANIELS

FLOWER ARRANGING FOR

THE AMERICAN HOME
(In Collaboration with Ruth Kistner)

STILLMEADOW KITCHEN

THE BOOK OF STILLMEADOW

Especially Father

BY

GLADYS TABER

A Pine Street Press Reprint Edition

PINE STREET PRESS
Baileys Harbor, Wisconsin

1979

A Pine Street Press Reprint Edition
Published by Pine Street Press
P. O. Box 302, Baileys Harbor, Wisconsin 54202 U.S.A.

Library of Congress Catalog Card No. 79-84304
ISBN: 0-915224-04-6

Contents

CONTENTS

TO ROB

PROLOGUE

THE LITTLE RED LEATHER BABY SHOES WERE CRACKED WITH
time and the pointed toes were dry and powdery. So I took
them in to be dipped in bronze.

All the salesmen admired them, gathered around to say,
"We seldom see any like these! Where did they come from?"

Then it came to me that the little shoes could be pre-
served in bronze, and labeled, but who was to recall the days
when they were worn, who would remember the lost and
faraway period which after all was only yesterday?

And I knew suddenly that I did not want the family to be
forgotten. Especially Father.

No, nor the time to be lost either. For history records the
large events or the general condition of society, but only
an individual can put down the way of life in a small town,
the excitements of an old-fashioned summer colony, the
days when nice girls came in at half-past ten.

Father and Mother were babies when the little red shoes
were the correct children's wear; already by the time I was
born, the toes broadened, the stiff soles softened.

But the family was still a tight-closed unit, children had
not begun to talk of leading their own lives.

Radio had not invaded the house, no planes drummed in
the sky, and the sound of war was not in any ears. The ice-
man still drove up in the damp cool wagon, and the gas
burner had only lately given way to the electric chandelier.

I began to go back in my memory to those summer vacations at the Bay. For that was the beginning of the time
when I first saw my parents, especially Father, as individuals.
Vivid as lightning on a summer day, the time came back to
me, and I knew it had to be written down. For many people
have years to remember in the same lost period.

Father's life unfolded in my mind, but not as a chrono-
logical series of events, rather in the natural order of my
recognizance. And that was the way I set down his story.

[9]

Father wouldn't have liked it for a moment.

"Skipping about like that," he would say, "without any order—it doesn't make sense and it is not right!"

But Father never held a high opinion of anything I wrote. He did have a kind of embarrassed pride in seeing my name in print, but he always said, "I suppose that it is all right to make up sort-of love stories, but they don't amount to anything. I can't see why anybody prints them."

I didn't argue. Arguing with him was a lost cause, as I well knew.

Later on, the day came when I found that I could not keep up with my writing and go on teaching, since both were full time jobs by now. I told Father so with a mild hope that he would be pleased about my career.

"You give up the writing," he said firmly, "and stick to teaching. That amounts to something!"

For almost the first time I disregarded his advice, and when he realized that I had made my choice, he put forth a last effort to improve me.

"Why don't you write about something good?" he asked. "Why don't you write about the diamond mines in South Africa? Or write about the gold up there on God's Lake?"

"But I've never been there, Papa," I said hopelessly.

"Well, I have," he said, "I can tell you just what you ought to write about."

But I felt that life in a small town with Father was far more exciting than anything I might find the world over.

And I still think it was!

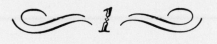

A Man's Castle

FATHER REALLY STARTED THE WHOLE THING WHEN HE GOT into his personal feud with Mr. Doolittle.

Mr. Doolittle was the Superintendent of the State Park which stretched for miles along the curving shore of Green Bay in Door County. And the reason we came in contact with him was that there was an adjacent small wedge of land which the State had never bought, due to the appropriation running out.

This piece of land lay between the Park and the village, and was privately owned. It lay under the cliff and facing the bay, and it was laid out in six plots. The road at the top of the cliff belonged to the Park. The cottagers owned from the road down to the water.

Father said they owned the water too.

The Coopers had the land nearest the village, then came the Church's. They both built large log houses. The Thompsons came next, with a smaller brown cottage. Father's place was next in line, and he owned three lots. He built his own cottage and a smaller one which was to be for my use, to entertain my friends and keep my own books in. Eventually when I married, this was deeded to me for my summer home.

And immediately beyond my land lay the State Park.

This was wild and lovely land, some of it virgin timber, some abandoned farmland. There were steep lonely cliffs plunging to the frost-green water, and there were still upland meadows sweet with wild strawberries and here and there an ancient house dreamed away the years.

There were also camp sites for tenters, and picnic sites furnished with those bench and table combinations that inevitably tipped over when someone sat on one side.

Many a potato salad has descended in my lap when Father got up suddenly from across one of those tables. You had to be quick to anticipate his movements.

Deeper in the woods wandered old Indian trails, and mint-cool springs broke through dark roots, and forgotten blackberry thickets dropped ripe fruit.

And over this paradise presided Mr. Doolittle, a tall, thin, weathered man with slow country speech and a strong mind. He was an able guardian, patrolling the Park roads constantly, watching the campers, keeping the picnic sites clean, trucking away garbage and rubbish. He lived in the midst of the Park on a piece of the best farmland, taking up too much of it, Father thought.

For Father really wanted to own the State Park himself. He had a strong personal prejudice against the State of Wisconsin at that time anyway. He did not like LaFollette. He reserved his strongest epithet "confounded" for that confounded group in Madison who were, he said, just a bunch of radicals.

Mr. Doolittle was the nearest State official, and whenever he drove past, Father remembered "that bunch in Madison." Then too, Mr. Doolittle cut down some of 'the biggest trees in one area of the State land, and Father was furious. It took the Creator a hundred years to grow those giants, and who was Mr. Doolittle to chop them down?

When Mr. Doolittle further built a camp site very near to our property, Father wanted to take the matter up with Washington. He was, he said, a taxpayer and a citizen. He had rights. (Father was the most unreconciled taxpayer I ever knew.)

"That man is out to ruin the land," he predicted ominously. "Campers all over everything, stealing things and setting fire to the woods."

"But, Papa," I said, "we camped in the Park ourselves while the cottages were being built."

"That was different," he said.

There were numerous hiking and riding trails in the Park which Mr. Doolittle kept expanding. And this was the reason for the real trouble.

For the beach in front of the cottages was the only easy access from the village to those trails. Fiends for exercise, of course, could go along the cliff-top road, miles farther. The tar road was hot and sticky in the blazing sun. You had to dodge automobiles, too. It was much better to go along the path the cottagers had, on the springy pine needles and with the cool water right at hand. This is what everyone did, and a steady procession began passing by under our front windows.

That summer was a hot one, and several times these passersby helped themselves to Father's ginger ale, in the spring box on the beach. Being a geologist, he had located the biggest and best and coldest spring along the whole shore, and purchased that particular site, dynamited the bushes and developed the flow.

[13]

People used to come a long way to dip that clear icy water and gather the crisp watercress at the edge. In those early innocent days, few cottages had plumbing, and the only available electricity was by means of Delco units. The natives did not deliver ice. So the spring was a great boon. Friends carried jugs of water from it, Father had a locked spring box in the overflow and our butter and cream were frosty. The Thompsons kept all their milk, eggs and butter there too, and the other cottagers left ginger ale and soda pop bottles below the box.

When bottles of ginger ale began to disappear from the spring, Father was furious, He made several large NO TRESPASSING signs and put them up. He began a BEWARE THE DOG card, but our mild and social Irish setter Timmie was so obviously charmed to greet the trespassers that he gave that up.

They continued to stream by day and night. They stumbled past with flashlights or lanterns after late beach picnics, giggling and knocking things over. The light shone directly in our front windows.

"This has got to stop!" Father shouted, after being waked up by one noisy group.

He called a meeting of the cottagers and proposed action. They should build a barbed wire fence across Mr. Cooper's land, said Father, running well out into the water. A second fence on my land would seal off the whole beach.

Mr. Church, a quiet, peaceful man, wondered whether it was legal to fence Green Bay. He mentioned riparian rights.

"It's our own property," declared Father, "if the land is ours, the water is ours too."

[14]

Mr. Cooper, the business man, wondered whether the villagers would object, and Miss Thompson, who was a history teacher, said why not compromise and just build a *small* fence half way to the beach?

Mamma said the tourist season was about over anyway.

"We don't want to stir up any trouble with anybody," said Mr. Church. "Not that it isn't a great nuisance to have all these people going and coming."

"We must put a stop to it," said Father, "why they even come on my beach and pick up my own stones!"

This reminded Mr. Church that he had found a queer stone on his beach and he brought it out. Instantly diverted, Father took the stone in his square strong hand and turned it over lovingly.

"Do you know how old this stone is?" he asked Mr. Church.

Mr. Church had not the foggiest idea.

Father told him. He told him where it had come from and how it got to Mr. Church's beach and this led him to a brief lecture on the wonders of the glacial period. His quick blue eyes were shining, his light, rather high voice deepened. For half an hour he talked, and everyone listened. The lamp light flickered on his rosy child-clear skin now flushed with excitement, and on his exuberantly curly light brown hair.

When he had polished off the ice age, he came back to Mr. Doolittle and his mouth tightened.

"I shall tell Mr. Doolittle this traipsing has to stop," he said. "I'll settle it, once and for all. I'll deliver our ultimatum."

"Well, it might be a good idea to talk it over," said Mr. Church. "The fence seems a little impractical."

Father went off the next morning. He bolted his usual breakfast of shredded wheat with crumpled bacon in it, scrambled eggs, toast, jelly, a banana and three cups of coffee with sugar and cream.

"Now don't get mad," said Mamma, "just speak to him quietly."

"I'm not mad," said Father, flushing. "I only intend to point out to him that this has got to stop. My beach is not a thoroughfare for all the tourists in Wisconsin. This ramjamming past has got to stop."

"Oh, dear, I hope Rufus keeps calm," Mamma said to me without hope.

He was gone all morning. When he got back, his mouth was pinned tight. In repose, his mouth was soft and sweet, almost too pretty for a man, but his habit of drawing the upper lip down and pinching it over the underlip gave him a look of granite severity.

"How did you come out?" asked Mamma, putting down her knitting.

"That man," Father said furiously, "that man ought to be shot! It's a disgrace. The taxpayers' money— That man—"

He bounded into the bedroom and came out in ten seconds with his bathing suit on. He pulled his old white shirt over it and rolled up the sleeves, speechless with rage. Father was too modest to wear his bathing suit without a shirt over it.

He rushed out the back door and we heard him chopping furiously.

"Oh, dear," said Mamma, "I hope he wasn't insulting

[16]

to Mr. Doolittle." She sighed. "What's he doing now? You look out and see."

"He's building the fence," I reported. "He's cutting fence posts out of the best trees in the yard."

"Mr. Doolittle isn't going to like it," said Mamma.

Father built the fence on my land, running it far out into the water. It was hard work but he pounded the big posts deep. Then he sat back, satisfied. The hikers could just go round by the road, he said. He'd settled it, once and for all.

For two days they did.

The second night, Father began worrying about *that* too. We all kept our cars up at the top of the cliff, and Father began to fear for their safety. He lighted a lantern and kept bounding up the cliff to be sure the hikers weren't stealing his tires.

"You can't trust those summer people," he said, after one wild scramble.

"Well, they're just like we are," said Mamma.

"Nonsense, we aren't summer people," said Father, "we just spend the winter somewhere else. We're residents."

He went back to his daily occupation when the fence was done. His job was to move most of the lake boulders from where God had placed them to other locations chosen by Father. He was constructing a boat dock that summer, and had already moved tons of rock, poured gallons of concrete. When finished, the dock could have accommodated an ocean-going vessel. Our small rowboat looked odd riding beside the massive rampart, and people used to stop and stare. The end was so large that Father finally built a fireplace on it and we had supper there and watched the sunset. Mamma and I watched the sunset, rather, while Father waded around below us, moving just a couple more boulders.

Father was happily working at his dock that day, clad in his bathing suit and shirt and a pair of old shoes to protect his sensitive feet. He had just heaved an enormous boulder up in his arms when he looked up and saw three men on horseback riding along his beach.

Behind them came two girls, also on horseback, cantering gaily past Miss Thompson's territory onto ours. There they deployed, for Father had taken out so many trees there was plenty of room. They brushed the front steps of the cottage. Mamma was sitting on the porch, momentarily resting from the dynamics of her household. She looked right into the face of a horse and screamed.

Father, mobilized instantly, pounded up the slope. Something in the silent fury of that compact short figure with long white shirt tails streaming startled the horses and the riders so they fled wildly on.

Past my cottage they raced, over the fence, and into the shelter of the Park.

Father didn't even change his wet clothes. He grabbed the car keys and bucketed up the cliff. The motor thundered.

"Oh, dear," said Mamma, "Mr. Doolittle is not going to like this at all." She got up from the swing. "Run down and bring up that steak in the spring box," she said. "This is the night for it."

Father was gone a long time. The placating odor of cinnamon rolls and apple turnover was in the air when he came in, but he was too mad to notice it. He was so mad he couldn't speak. Mamma went over and got Mr. Church, and eventually they found out that Mr. Doolittle had made a new riding trail beginning just beyond my land, and put up signs urging riders to use it. Further, he had told Father the fence must come down. There was an old road running along the beach, he said, and this was to continue the riding trail.

The cottagers met that evening. Everyone was ready to give up, accommodate themselves to the nuisance. Everyone but Father. He, strengthened with steak, mashed potatoes, gravy, new peas, apple turnover and a few cinnamon rolls, was ready to fight to the death.

"You sign a paper," he said, "and all agree. I'll see the Town Clerk. There must be justice, even in Wisconsin under the LaFollette gang."

"But it's hopeless," said Mr. Cooper. "We can't fight Mr. Doolittle's authority. And it's not like a city up here. Look at poor Professor Moss who's been trying thirty years to get the title straight on his land. And Dr. Reeve has had that fishing shack on his beach at least sixteen years, and the man won't move it or let him move it—and what can you do?"

Father went to the Town Clerk. Then he went to Sturgeon Bay. In the end, he discovered that if a road were not used as a road for a certain number of years, it could be declared outlawed.

So he drove the rest to join him and they went to the Town Council. By this time, Mr. Doolittle was thoroughly enraged. There was a terrible session at the Council. Then they got up a petition and wangled around with it. It took half the summer to get it through and they all had to pay a neat sum, which Father said was simply graft for the unscrupulous radicals in Madison.

In September they got the road off the records and the land was the cottagers' again.

We all took a long breath. Mamma said she came to the cottage to rest and relax and she hadn't had a minute's peace so far, and vacation was nearly over, and she hoped Father would now settle down.

Mamma was a quiet person, the joy of battle was not in her. But Father went about with an air of conscious virtue. He had won a hard victory and all was well. He went back to his boulders.

None of the thousand on his own beach was just right that particular day, so he moved across the line onto the sacred precincts of Mr. Doolittle. This brought him to the camp site where he found Mr. Doolittle's men busily erecting a large log cabin for a communal kitchen. Something to attract all the tourists in the state!

Father boiled home. Mr. Doolittle's revenge was a neat one. Father had won the battle of the pathway, but Mr. Doolittle would fill the camp site with travelers. Mr. Church and Mr. Cooper agreed that nothing could be done about the state property, whatever Mr. Doolittle decided was law there.

Father loaded his revolver and went out to shoot the heads off any unwary pine snakes. His mouth was tight and his face flushed. The iron had entered his soul.

He was gone an hour or so, and then he came loping back. He rounded the corner of the porch smiling. When Father smiled, it was like the sun coming out, and spring and summer in your heart.

"Grace," he said, "where is all that garbage?"

"Well," said Mamma, "I'm glad you got around to it. Before we get typhoid."

"I'll take care of it," said Father happily, "right now! Come with me, Gladys!"

Garbage was a constant nightmare at the bay. To bury it you had to practically dynamite a hole in the rock strata. There was, in those days, no town dump, no garbage disposal, no anything. If it happened to be cool, you burned it in the fireplace. Sometimes we lugged it all over the peninsula looking for an unsuspecting pig, but there were few farms, mostly cherry orchards and woods. Sometimes Father rowed out and dumped it in the bay, but he didn't like this, it troubled his New England conscience. He did not like water pollution and he rowed so far out that several times he got caught by a storm and barely made it back to land.

Especially now we had tons of garbage. The late melons were in, and Father loved melons. A pile of rinds three feet high was in the barrel, also a few bushels of corncobs.

"Can't you find me a little more?" asked Father.

He stowed it all in cartons in the back seat of the car.

"Are you going to try the big swamp?" I asked. I loved the big swamp, the tamaracks grew there, delicately green and feather-soft, and the air was hot and still. In season, the faint pink of lady slippers pricked the shadows.

I loved to pick them, but Father wasn't interested in anything except fossilized ferns in the plant world.

"It's too far to the swamp," he said now, turning into the State Park.

"Then where are we going?"

"Wait and see!"

He bumped along the woodroad and turned to the camp site.

"What are you doing, Papa?" I asked.

"Wait and see," he said again. He stopped the car, bounced out and began to unload the cartons.

"Now you just watch," he said, "and if you see Mr. Doolittle's truck, you blow the horn!"

"Oh, Papa," I wailed.

But he was up to the eyebrows in melon rinds as he leaped nimbly toward the big State disposal cans. He was grinning.

Our garbage filled the big containers. After the last load Father whisked back into the car and we roared away.

"There," said Father, "that will show him!"

He was on top again.

About five days later, Mr. Doolittle came to the cottage. I saw him first and called Mamma, Mr. Doolittle looked mad. Father was out in the water, as usual, bent double over a boulder the size of a freight car. The day was quite cold, so he had on his long white underwear, then the bathing suit, and then the shirt. Mamma had protested against the underwear but he told her it was just the thing, and then she wouldn't have to wash it.

When Mamma called him, he came out of the water like a strange Triton. He ran up the beach, but that was natural for he never walked.

Even in Commencement processions he was always gaining on the man ahead of him.

His shirt was soaked, and clung to the underwear, his curly hair dripped. But he faced Mr. Doolittle with intense dignity. "And what is your business now?" he asked.

Mr. Doolittle snorted. "The garbage," he said. "I find we are having to send an extra truck twice a week to carry the garbage away from the camp site next to your property. More garbage than the campers would accumulate in a year." He glared.

Father glared back.

"Someone," said Mr. Doolittle, "is using the State containers for private garbage. This has to be stopped."

Father threw up his head. "Do I understand, Mr. Doolittle, that the camp site is for the public, or for your personal friends?"

"It is a public camp site," began Mr. Doolittle, getting very red, "but . . ."

"Then," said Father, "can you inform me, sir, why as a public taxpayer I am not entitled to use a public container?"

Mr. Doolittle choked. "It is not a town dump," he said, "it is for the use of campers. The State takes care of the Park for the benefit of the campers."

"By cutting down the best timber ever grown," said Father, "as anybody but those idiots in Madison would know! Do you realize how long it took to grow that stand of pines you decimated last week?"

"We are opening a new site," Mr. Doolittle found himself on the defensive. With Father this always happened. "We need more room for the campers."

[23]

"And the pine makes good fence posts for your land," added Father keenly.

"Now, Doctor," Mr. Doolittle raised his voice above a shout, "I only came here to tell you that you can't dump your garbage in the State cans and if you do, I'll have you arrested. That's all!" and he retreated up the steps to the top of the cliff.

Father grinned.

He kept right on carrying the garbage to the camp site. He went at dusk when Mr. Doolittle would be at supper. Then he went early in the morning. Mr. Doolittle tried his best to catch him, but he never did. And if any of the campers saw a short vigorous man in a white shirt lugging a full garbage can to the State containers, they only thought a new camper had moved in.

Mamma tried to diminish the amount, but we had a lot of company, and many fried chickens.

We heard that the campers were complaining because so many skunks came nightly to the camp. Father was too upright a Methodist to lure the skunks, but it wasn't his fault if the most choice bits of garbage happened to be on top of the cans and the lids were loose.

By now, he and Mr. Doolittle were not on speaking terms, and it was almost time to think about going home. Mamma hoped everything was over and winter's absence might make the heart grow fonder.

But then Mr. Doolittle installed a water pump in the bay right beside my beach, to pump water up the cliff to the golf course. The pump made a noise like elephants crashing through brush, but that was nothing compared to the noise Father made when he heard it.

The Coopers had gone, and the Church's were packing. Miss Thompson opined that it would rain all next summer and the pump would be disconnected. But Father went down in the cold September moonlight and disconnected the pump himself. It took a day or so for Mr. Doolittle to discover this, and he had no proof at all as to who tampered with it. He started it up again, and Father promptly cut it off.

"I have to have my sleep," he said firmly.

"Let's go home," said Mamma, "and have a little peace."

Mr. Doolittle fixed the pump again.

One Saturday afternoon Mamma was giving the last tea of the season. She had begged Father to attend, but he said he was too busy to sit around all afternoon and rock. He had to get his dock fixed up for winter. No dock in the bay except the big Chicago boat dock ever had withstood the ice shove, but his was going to. Provided his family left him alone and he had a few more bags of Portland cement.

Father had been off in the rowboat selecting some choice boulders on a distant beach, State owned. He came rowing in just as Mama was pouring tea on the front porch.

He made a striking picture. The boat was loaded to the last inch and Father had his underwear-bathing suit-shirt costume, plus an old straw hat. As he jumped in the water and began to warp his overloaded craft to the dock, Mr. Doolittle appeared, and he was smiling a dangerous and meaningful smile.

He set his feet on the sacred cement of the dock, and walked out. Leaning over, he addressed Father.

Mamma went pale, and dropped her teaspoon, and excused herself as she hurried down to the dock.

[25]

Father was leaping up and down in the water, waving his arms.

"What is it?" Mamma asked Mr. Doolittle.

"I just stopped by," he said, "to tell you I had occasion to check the survey of this property adjoining the State's."

"Survey?" asked Mamma blankly. Father was incoherent.

"I find the lines of your land are incorrectly followed," Doolittle said grandly, "and a portion of your daughter's cottage is on State property!"

"Well," said Mamma comfortably, "get the man to straighten them out."

"I'm afraid it's not that simple," he said. And he withdrew as Father dredged himself out of the water. Father flailed past and bounced onto the porch, saw the tea party guests, muttered and bounced back and vanished around the corner.

He could be heard quite plainly, though, through the thin walls. The tea party rapidly disbanded. Father whirled past them on his way to the Church's, giving them a wild glance, but no greeting.

When he came home, an hour later, he was in the same frame of mind with which his ancestors faced the British.

"Now, Papa, you'll raise your blood pressure," warned Mamma, "I am sure it's nothing serious. Mr. Doolittle can't cut off Gladys' kitchen."

"Serious!" Father roared, "Not serious? Do you realize just what this means? It means that one corner of our cottage is built on Lillian Thompson's land?"

"Mercy," said Mamma. She sat down, and clasped her hands.

[26]

"And a piece of Mr. Cooper's bathroom is on Mr. Church's property," went on Father.

"But I don't see why . . ."

"And Mr. Church's pump house," he continued, "is on Miss Lillian's land on the other side? And as for Gladys—" he waved at me, "you know what else happens on that side?"

"No. What?" asked Mamma.

"The outhouse," he said heavily, "is on the State land."

It was true, the whole horrid thing was true. Without Mr. Doolittle's feud with Father we might have all gone happily to our graves with wedges of other people's houses on our own land. But now it was all in the open. Nobody could ever sell, if they wanted to. Nobody could buy, either.

A rapid trip thirty miles to Green Bay to the record office disclosed the unhappy fact that the lots were supposed to run from the cliff to the beach, not in normal straight lines, but slantwise!

The lot owners had merely established the top stake and run the lines to the beach as a sane person might, and built accordingly. But the upper peninsula lines were never sane, and as it was, everyone had sliced off someone else's land.

We had all lived peacefully, except for outside alarms, cutting down one another's trees, hammering up shutters on somebody else's cottage windows, but now Mr. Doolittle had ruined all that.

"Suppose one of us dies," Father demanded, "and the land was sold? What would happen?"

"We're all very healthy," said Mamma.

It was Mr. Doolittle's day. He emphasized it by suggesting the state might take over the whole area anyway, meanwhile we were all living highly illegal lives.

The problem of my outhouse was the worst. The cliff ran practically into my house, and the only small level spot now was not mine at all. I wondered whether we could suspend the outhouse from the cliffside. Otherwise it would have to go by the front steps.

"There is absolutely no way out of this," said Miss Lillian in tears, "and I've put all my savings into this place. What shall I do?"

Mr. Cooper, advised by long distance phone, came back to see what could be done now. There was another meeting of the landowners. Everyone was discouraged.

"We can manage it," said Father firmly.

"How?" asked Mr. Church.

"Everything was all right when the lines ran straight," explained Father, "or when we thought they ran straight. So all we do now is simply change them back from where they really are to where we have always thought they were! That will fix Mr. Doolittle!" He paused a moment to let his words sink in.

"They ought to be straight anyway," he said, "it's ridiculous to angle them off."

"How can we do that?" asked Miss Lillian.

"We just speak to the Town Council, and there you are," said Father.

They drew up a paper forthwith and signed it and Mr. Cooper went back to St. Louis. There was still the small matter of my outhouse and the Park, but nobody mentioned that.

But it developed that changing the lines was not so simple. Not quite a matter of name signing. The State of Wisconsin was involved. I could, it developed, neither

present my outhouse to Mr. Doolittle, nor persuade him
to give it back to me. A surveyor brought up from Sturgeon
Bay, at quite an expense, climbed around a full day, running lines back and forth and up and down. He said that
straightening the lines in the casual way Father wanted,
would sheer off a third of my land.

I was a worn and willing sacrifice by now. I would give
up, I said, the whole end of my cottage and live on the front
porch just to get it settled. But not Father. I was not to be
deprived of a single inch of pine needles.

Mr. Doolittle was as adamant. He wanted the state line
run exactly where it was supposed to be. No compromise
was possible.

After two weeks of frantic struggle the Church's gave up
and went home. The Thompsons left too. Father drove
down to college registration but right back the same night.
Every day he covered thirty miles to Sturgeon Bay to badger
the record office and the state officials. Mamma wanted to
go home. I was missing all the pre-school parties.

On a Friday night Father came back from a last battle
with the county.

"Now," said Mamma, "you may as well give this up and
let us go home. I don't see why we can't go on as we are
anyway. Mr. Doolittle isn't going to saw off half the cottage."

Father looked at her stonily. "We will never give in," he
said. "We will take it to the state legislature. We'll go to
Madison!" He added bitterly, "Much as I hate to deal with
a bunch of radicals."

"You can't possibly do that!" said Mamma incautiously.

"Oh, yes, I can," said Father. "Come on, pack up and

let's get started. If I go to Madison on Monday I may get things rolling before classes start."

The following summer the legislature of the State of Wisconsin passed the petition of five obscure taxpayers up on the peninsula to adjust their boundaries. I don't suppose the august body paid much attention, and if any voice was raised to ask about the state line, there was no echo.

The stakes were replaced where we had always had them.

I now hung my washing on land that belonged to the sovereign State of Wisconsin and my outhouse sat amiably on a plot of public land, but I didn't mind.

It was August of that second summer when Father came in one day and laid the roll of blueprints in Mamma's lap.

"There," he said, "I hope you're satisfied."

Mamma had been so passive a figure in the whole thing that she looked at him with surprise. "I thought things were all right the way they were," she said, "and after all this to-do we're right back where we were again, aren't we?"

It was a very still afternoon and the Chicago boat was gliding softly across the bay in the long lovely summer light.

Father stared out at it, his lips tight. The air was soft as silk, the great cliffs were in green shadow. Miss Lillian and her sister were out in their red canoe, paddling quietly along in the shallow water. It was as peaceful as a Corot, though not as misty.

"I am glad it's all over," said Mamma. "I hope we can have a little peace for a change. I do wish that you had left Mr. Doolittle alone in the first place and not stirred all this up!"

"I?" said Father, "I leave Mr. Doolittle alone? Do you

mean to imply that I had anything to do with all this trouble?"

"Well," said Mamma, "we were quite all right until you started fencing off the beach."

"That's right," said Father, who was tired out. "My fault. Everything is always my fault. That's the thanks I get for saving our home. I suppose you'd like it if Mr. Doolittle took over all we own, lock, stock and barrel."

"Now don't get excited," Mamma spoke calmly. "I said I was glad it was all over. And I'm sure nobody else could have handled the legislature alone as well as you did."

"Quite a surprise for Mr. Doolittle," said Father, mollified.

"But let's not have any more trouble from now on," said Mamma. "I think if you will just not try to upset Mr. Doolittle, we shall be much better off."

"I haven't done a thing," said Father, "but save our home."

"Yes," said Mamma.

We sat down to supper. Mamma had laid the cloth on the porch table so we could see the sunset while we ate. The sky was copper rose and the water violet overlaid with a glaze of gold.

Far out, a small sail angled against the horizon. Across the bay, on the headland that drove out to the deep water, the lights of the village began to glow and the white church was like colored pearl against the cedar green.

Mamma had hot biscuits with the smothered steak, and fresh sweet corn and watercress salad and a nice lattice-top cherry pie. There we sat, a nice little American family in an idyllic setting enjoying the peace and quiet of the shore.

Then Father laid down his knife and looked at Mamma, his eyes shining their brightest blue.

"You know what?" he said, "I've had an idea! I think I'll make you a sand beach."

"A sand beach?" Mamma was dazed.

"There's a nice sand beach," said Father, "over in the Park just beyond Doolittle's. I think I'll just row over there a few times and move the sand here. If I make two or three trips a day, it won't take any time at all."

Mamma braced herself. "But this beach is all right!"

"Stony," said Father. "No good for bathing." He reached for his fourth or fifth biscuit and poured clover honey on it.

"A nice sandy beach," said Father, "is just what we need!"

The Great Endeavor

IT WAS OUR THIRD SUMMER AT THE BAY WHEN FATHER DE-cided to create a sand beach. Mamma had not taken the idea seriously when he first dreamed it up, because he had a way of planning projects which did not materialize. One of them, for instance, was the mink farm, and one was a wild duck business. They were not projects adapted to life on a college campus or at a summer cottage either, and most of them involved an outlay of cash to begin with and that settled it. For Father was never, never impractical when it came to laying out cash.

"I wouldn't risk a red cent on it," he would say of most investments. "Not a red cent."

But the sandy beach wouldn't cost anything if he simply took all the sand from the State Park and moved it by his own labor to our shore. There was, on all that rocky penin-sula, a single cove where the sand was like an ocean beach, and this was in the middle of the State Park property.

On our own beach, the stones ranged in size from small boulders to huge wagon-wheel shapes. We wore tennis shoes when we went in swimming and leaped precariously from rock to rock. We could row over to the sand beach if we wanted to, but that was too easy for Father. Much better to have a nice sandy beach right at our front door.

ESPECIALLY FATHER

"I don't see why we can't just have a nice vacation like other people do," said Mamma. "Why do you always keep on working at things so? You never rest a minute all winter long, and in summer you nearly kill yourself."

It was true that winter was like the center of a whirlpool at our house. When Father was teaching geology at the small college, he was also rushing off to locate artesian wells for paper companies, inspect probable gold mines, or investigate oil wells. In his spare time, he worked on fossils, wrote articles, strewed the house with specimens for collections.

The place was overrun with students, and Mamma never knew how many people would sit down to supper when six o'clock came.

Father would just bring a couple of boys with him when he came from the college, or meet someone on the way home and ask them to have supper.

Some women might not have been able to stretch meals as easily as Mamma could, but she was never at a loss. Even with no deep freeze or electric refrigerator, and no frozen foods in the market, Mamma managed to feed five or six on a moment's notice. She had an old gas stove, and an emergency shelf for supplies—and she was a genius.

Father took her entirely for granted. He expected her to do all the housework, keep his shirts in order, give the best parties in the faculty, do most of the family errands.

Mamma did all this and much more all during my childhood. She made a good many of our clothes, stitched up draperies, hemmed sheets, knitted afghans, made patchwork quilts. She went to her clubs, helped run church suppers, attended all the lectures and concerts that ever were given in our town.

She was not exactly given to idleness.

She also helped Father edit all his papers, compose his speeches, locate mislaid specimens.

The original idea of building the cottages had been that we could settle down for a quiet summer. Mamma had tried summer vacations traveling with Father, and almost anything, she felt, was better than that. A person of ordinary strength did well to come back alive after a trip with Father. He was gifted with such alarming vitality and such a horror of wasting a moment of time. Even a short drive was exhausting for Mamma, for he drove like a madman and if spoken to about it said crossly, "We'll never get anywhere if we don't keep moving!"

Father went through life like a jet plane, and he expected everyone around him to do the same. Even now, if I sit down just to relax a minute, I have a jumpy feeling that I "ought to be doing something."

He never walked, he always ran. In winter he wore a heavy coat lined with fur and with a large fur collar that engulfed him. He did not button the coat, even when it was thirty below zero. He jogged across the campus with the coat belling out behind. In summer, he loped around with his white shirt soaked with perspiration from his speed.

So Mamma had been delighted at the idea of long dreamy summer days at the bay with Father reading quietly on the porch while she packed a casual picnic lunch. He would have to rest, she thought. There was not even land enough for a garden.

But the first summer he had spent chopping wood. Every day, all day, he chopped. He cleared the woods around the cottage, cut trees into fireplace lengths, dynamited stumps. He adored dynamiting. Mamma never knew at what instant his voice would sing out, "Stand back! She's going!" and a cedar stump would fly past and crash on the cottage roof.

On the hottest day, the sound of his axe shattered the stillness. On the quietest afternoon, our beach was a constant explosion. He could fell a tree, too, and have it fall to the inch of where he wanted it.

Mamma thought this would be a temporary thing, the trees would be cleared the first season. But as soon as they were, he decided to clear up the front of the land. It was studded with large, deeply embedded boulders. Mamma said there was no earthly reason for them to be disturbed. "It will be smoother," said Father firmly.

He dug up hundreds of boulders and with them built a foundation for the front porch, massive enough to support the Empire State Building.

Then casting about restlessly, he thought of the dock and the following long vacations he worked from dawn to dusk building the great dock. Now and then, he got a native to help a little, but they always gave up after a few days and went home to rest. Father was too much for them. Mamma pointed out that we didn't need a dock for one small rowboat. Father said some people would appreciate a nice dock, even if she didn't.

Hundreds of boulders, tons of cement went into that dock, and it wasn't Father's fault that as soon as he finished it the water level of the great lakes dropped a few feet and the dock was a monument on dry land.

THE GREAT ENDEAVOR

Mamma elected me to lure him into fishing to occupy him. First we took a day to drive to Sturgeon Bay for tackle, and he got all the kinds there were, including muskie equipment, although nobody ever caught a muskie in our waters.

Then he dug bait. It was worth watching. He bent double and rammed the shovel in the resistant earth, flailed the dirt up in wide fans, and pounced rapidly on the luckless worms. He was not satisfied with a few worms, he had to have a pailful. Then he rushed to the water and dragged up half the minnow population.

Then we got in the rowboat as best we could with the load of equipment, rods, reels, landing nets, lures, worms, and minnows.

We went in the midday, the hottest time of all, because we were ready, and Father wasn't going to kowtow to the fish by going when they might like to bite better. After all his effort, he felt a fish should be glad to bite any time.

Father wore a pair of old volleyball pants, high laced tennis shoes, a long-sleeved white shirt, a straw hat. He tied a handkerchief around his neck, for he was already sweating profusely.

"Now you row, Gladys," he said, "I'll get the lines ready, and direct you."

He heaved up the anchor, which was a large pail filled with cement, and would have moored anything up to the *Queen Mary*.

"Hurry up," he said sharply, "if we don't get started, we'll never get back."

He picked out a spot at least a mile away, and I rowed. Then he decided that wasn't quite the best place after all, and had me row around the curve of the bay to another spot. I was getting pretty hot and tired.

"This looks fine, Papa." I said.

"Hush," he said, "the fish will hear you!"

He leaned over until the boat tipped dangerously. His bright blue eyes were intent, his curly hair was damp, his clear rosy skin was flushed.

"I don't see anything," he said. "Just row on around the next bend."

"But, Papa," I said.

"Row faster," he said impatiently. "We'll never get anywhere at this rate!"

I rowed faster. My middy was sodden, my hair fell over my face.

"What's the matter?" he said. "You seem a little weak!"

In half an hour we reached another spot, looking just like the first two, except that it was, of course, further from home.

"Why don't we try here?" I asked.

"Fishing," he said, "takes patience. You have to go where the fish are. There's a submerged dock somewhere around here—they like old docks."

"Shall I row on?" I mopped my face and looked at the blisters on my hands.

"Just a little farther." He leaned over. "There, you've rowed right past it! Row back! Row quietly, the fish will hear you!"

I rowed dizzily back, I knew better than to argue. But I thought of a lot of things I would say to Mamma when I got home.

"Hold it!" said Father suddenly. He heaved the anchor.

I sagged back in the seat. Now I could catch my breath, I thought.

We dropped our lines. We sat for two minutes in the blazing sun with the boat motionless, then Father jerked his line up, inspected the hook and bait. "Wonder what's wrong," he said, "they aren't biting!"

He changed from a worm to a minnow and dropped his line again. An instant later, he whipped it up again and changed to a lure. "Something is wrong," he said. "Can't sit here all day! Row on around the next cliff."

The anchor boiled up and we were off again. It seemed to me we quartered the whole bay. We passed other boats with motionless fishermen in them. We were almost run down by a sailboat because Father wouldn't let me change our course.

"It's their business to keep out of our way," he said firmly.

They heeled past just scraping us.

We anchored four or five times just long enough to wet the lines and change the bait and pull the lines up again.

"No use," he said. "We may as well go home. Can't you row any faster?"

"No," I said sullenly, "I can't."

"Then move over," he said. He hopped the length of the boat almost turning it over and grabbed the oars. We skimmed along. Father rowed as if he were in the Harvard shell and the race was on.

"Fishing," he said, "is just a waste of time anyway. Nothing to show for all that effort."

"Papa," I said, "I see something swimming out there off our shore."

"Nonsense, just a deadhead," he said. "Nobody goes out that far."

"But it's moving!" I insisted.

Father turned then, and looked. His eyes were as good as binoculars and he gazed keenly, bent over the oars and they nearly cracked with the pull.

"It's that dog," he said.

I could see, then, that it was indeed that dog. Timothy, our Irish setter, was Father's dog when he was good, and my dog when he wasn't, and "that dog" when he made trouble. He had seen us from the shore, and filled with yearning to join the expedition had swum out. Mamma was making spiced cherry preserve and hadn't missed him.

He must have been a half mile off shore and he was pretty exhausted. Father rowed wildly. "Confounded idiot," he kept muttering.

The boat sped along, and we drew up near Timmie at last. Timmie made a wild lunge and tried to climb in the boat with us. Most of the tackle went overboard, together with the worm pail and Father's straw hat. One oar floated off. Timmie was a large strong setter and he was scared. Water sloshed in the boat.

"Stop that!" roared Father. "You'll swamp us!"

I burst into tears. It was evident Timmie couldn't get in the boat, he would drown. His desperate scrabbling paws would get weaker. Landing such a large animal in such a small craft was obviously impossible.

But not to Father. Impossible was a word he had no traffic with. He hooked his feet over the anchor pail and lowered the rest of his body over the side of the boat and laced his arms around Timmie.

[40]

"Lean to the right," he yelled at me. I leaned. It was nip and tuck for a moment with the balance on the tuck. Then with a powerful heave, Father and Timmie fell back in the boat together, with an extra pailful of water to boot. It didn't occur to me that it was an extraordinary feat to get all that dog in over the boat edge.

"There," said Father angrily, "let that teach you a lesson!"

Timmie was frantically kissing him. Father took the oar and paddled with it until he grabbed the lost oar.

"Bail out this boat," he said to me. "Don't just sit there!"

Mamma was on the beach when we came in. It was long past dinnertime and she knew that meals always clarioned Father from any pursuit. She decided we were drowned.

We came grandly in to the dock, a boatload of three sopping passengers, a lot of water, some sand, and no fish.

"My goodness," said Mamma, "why didn't you tell me you were taking Timmie? I might have worried!"

Timmie, rested and in his right mind now, leaped out and embraced her joyfully, soaking her clean print dress. I crawled out, aching and sunburned and blistered.

Father threw out the tired minnows and the worn worms.

"Did you catch anything?" asked Mamma tactlessly.

Father gave her a look. "Nothing but that confounded dog," he said. "Bay's all fished out. It's those summer people. Ruined it."

This was our last fishing trip. Father drove up to Gill's Rock and bought a carload of fish from the fishermen on the dock. And in a day or so, he got up from the breakfast table and said, "Well, I guess I'll move the sand beach over."

[41]

"But you can't!" wailed Mamma. "It isn't practical! It will only wash away! You can't just move beaches around!"

After that, nothing could have stopped him.

It wasn't his fault that it was Sunday when the great endeavor began.

"I want to go to church," said Mamma. "It's Sunday."

She loved the little white Moravian church in the village. The Scandinavian choir sang with such a rich sweet quality and the sermons were plain and peaceful. Moreover a number of Professors and their families who lived around the shore went to church, and the visiting on the clean steps afterward was pleasant. In the little summer colony those days, life was not geared to boogie-woogie and bridge, but to the delicate excitement of tea on the porch, a game of whist, and church on Sunday.

But Father said, "I better get started. First thing you know summer will be over, and you will go back to town without any beach at all."

He went off and borrowed a neighbor's rowboat and chained it to our own with a tire chain. It was a hot July day so he wore his bathing suit, the shirt, and panama hat. He loaded both boats with pails, a small washtub, a shovel, and one of Mamma's best cooking pans.

We watched him row out, his short compact figure bending over the oars as he put all his strength into every stroke. There was something lonely and determined about that figure in the boat with the second craft veering dizzily behind.

Mamma sat down and sighed. "Someday I suppose he'll kill himself," she said. "And there's nothing anybody can do about it."

She didn't often let herself go to that extent, but the sand beach was the last straw.

It was about two and a half miles to the sand beach which was quite a row in the summer heat. He would be gone quite awhile, so Mamma and I got dressed and went to church with the Thompsons. They were eating dinner across the bay, but we took a chance of a ride home with someone else.

How beautiful the little white village in the sunshine! How dark and deep the cedars on the cliff! The church lifted its spire at the top of the great rock ledge. The bay below was a shimmer of blue threaded by the green needle of Horseshoe Island. The sun shone through the window inside on the blonde braids of the girls and the wheat-gold hair of the men. And on my navy blue voile with the white starched collar and cuffs.

Mamma's soft brown hair was tucked well under the brim of her white straw, her small firm hands in the white gloves were folded neatly on her brown silk lap, her small feet were trim in their white slippers. Her brown eyes were shining, her lovely mouth curved with some dream.

I thought of Father rowing madly over the water and felt suddenly sad. Why couldn't he come with us, in a nice white flannel or palm beach suit like Dr. Reeve? Why did he want to move that sand beach? Maybe, I thought, if he could have preached the sermon, he would like church. But sitting passive was too much for him.

We lingered on the steps after the service, the women in their soft frilly dresses, white gloves, and hats of thin delicate straw with flowers or cherries on them, the men in

[43]

their good suits, the little girls in white muslin with colored ribbons, the small boys in starched white sailor suits.

Mamma said that Father was working. She blushed when she said so, because she knew it was giving the impression that he was writing a paper on foraminifera or something queer. The Walshes offered to drive us home, and Mamma instantly asked them to dinner. She just couldn't help asking anyone to dinner that was around, and Mamma being the cook she was, no one ever refused.

Dr. Walsh was a correct, early edition of a college Dean and Mrs. Walsh was one of those clubwomen who flit from D.A.R. to P.E.O. to Kappa Delta to goodness knows what else. They were so socially correct that they belonged to the end of the calling card era, and I thought they were dreadfully dull.

When we got home, Mamma excused herself and went to the kitchen where she got those heavenly meals on a three burner oil stove. I sat on the porch with the Walshes trying to converse like a lady. Mamma was pretty nervous because Father wasn't there. It was dinnertime and she had fully counted on his being in the cottage and in dry clean clothes for Sunday dinner.

Maybe he had gone for the paper at the Thompsons, she decided. He would turn up in a minute or so. Meanwhile she made the gravy and stirred the giblets in. The chicken was sending forth a divine smell from the top stove oven.

"You have a beautiful view," said Mrs. Walsh.

"I suppose it isn't really damp this near the water," said Dr. Walsh thoughtfully.

"And so restful," said Mrs. Walsh, "I suppose you spend most of the time sitting here and watching the water."

"What's that curious thing out there?" asked Dr. Walsh, pointing a long academic finger.

I stared. Oh, heavens, there came Father! The boat and its following boat were riding so low in the water that we could just make them out. Father was sitting with sand rising around him until he looked like an oasis. As he rowed, the boats staggered along.

"Why, it's a man in two boats!" said Dr. Walsh with surprise.

"It's Father," I said.

"What in the world is he doing? What's he got in that boat?" asked Mrs. Walsh lifting her eyeglasses and peering.

"He's just moving sand," I said feebly.

The Walshes got up and went right out the screen door down to the shore. Father was soaked and covered with uprooted water reeds. The panama had suffered a sea change and was brimless. He had a boatload of sand, all right, and he was burned lobster red. When he was near the dock, he jumped out and moved like a queer kind of waterbird behind his cargo, his shirt tails momentarily floating free.

Then he looked up and saw the Walshes, immaculate and elegant, staring at him. He waved a dirty paw.

"Hello," he said. "How did you get here?"

"What in the world are you doing?" asked Dr. Walsh.

Father looked up. "Making a sand beach," he said simply.

Dr. Walsh was aghast. "But you can't do that!" he cried. "You can't do that!"

"Don't see why not," said Father.

"It will all wash away," said Dr. Walsh.

"Not when I get through with it," predicted Father.

Mamma appeared on the steps. "You come right out of that water," she called, "and get ready for dinner. The dumplings will fall!"

That brought him. He straightened up with difficulty and climbed to the dock. "That stuff is heavy when it's wet," he said, and went flapping up to the bedroom for dry clothes.

After the Walshes were gone, Mamma said, "You'll disgrace us all. How did it look, you and that pair of boats coming in like that, and company here after church?"

"I suppose you'd like it better if I sat around and fanned myself all day like that lazy Walsh," said Father. "Some people never even care whether they accomplish anything or not." He was tired and cross. He added, "Of course I am not thanked for whatever I do for your own good."

"I don't want a sand beach," said Mamma.

Father got up and went down to the beach in a towering rage.

"Go and see if you can't get him to stop," said Mamma, "before he kills himself."

When I got to the beach Father was shoveling the sand from the boats.

"It's nice sand," I ventured.

He stopped and scooped a handful. "Beautiful sand," he agreed, "look at the particles! Think of the millions of years that the water has worked to make that sand! Think of the great streams rolling the boulders and pounding them together."

"Tell me about the inland sea," I said.

We sat on the edge of the dock and Father spun his

fairy tale science. He forgot the boats until it was too late to unload that day.

But the next day he was at it early, before I was up. And the following days were difficult. He was able to move only two or three loads a day and this made him angry. The trouble was that he could not row back with two boats filled with sand as fast as he rowed over. This upset his calculations. Then the shoveling of sand was pretty heavy, even for him, especially as it always seemed to get wet and weigh more. He complained that the wind was always against him and the borrowed rowboat wasn't worth a hill of beans. It didn't hold much.

He had a terrible sunburn, his sensitive skin was raw with it, and the fact that he was wet almost all day was not good for it either.

One day at the end of the week he came in and dropped on the porch swing. When he tried to get up, he groaned and fell back. Mamma put down her pan of potatoes and flew. No matter how rocky life with him might be, she was always ready to fly to his rescue.

"Oh, Rufus, you've strained your back!" she cried.

He groaned again, loudly, and lay flat. "I've got lumbago!" he said, "I've got lumbago!"

Mamma had his wet shoes off and was covering him with a blanket.

"It's all that shoveling sand," said Mamma, "and rowing like a lunatic all day."

"It's lumbago," said Father.

He was laid up until dinner was on the table, and then he rose and got to the table. He didn't make another trip that day, but he went off the next morning early and bought a new outboard motor and hooked it on his boat. It was faster, he said, than rowing.

Mamma was a little relieved. By now Father had moved enough sand to make appreciable small piles along the rocky beach. If you went swimming and stepped with extreme care, you could leap from one patch of sand to another, but it was tricky business because the spots seemed to shift about so.

By now the project was public business. Everyone in the summer colony advised and argued about it. The family Doctor came in to dissuade Father from such strenuous effort. He told Father he ought to take it easier, and Father said he only needed a bottle of liniment for his stiff joints.

The only thing the Doctor achieved was a temporary lull while we all drove over to Bailey's Harbor to see if there were any Indian mounds there. Father didn't shovel that day, nor row, but he galloped miles along the beach looking for Indian relics.

The next day he was chugging out again in the boat.

Mamma was in hourly terror of Mr. Doolittle, who might not want state sand moved to our private beach, but Father was pleased at the thought of getting ahead of Mr. Doolittle.

The summer lengthened again, the nights grew cold, and Mamma began airing blankets and scrubbing closets. Father couldn't help, he was too busy moving sand.

But now a terrible conflict arose in his constantly damp bosom, for he always spent the last days at the cottage in rock-lugging for the dock, getting ready for the winter ice shove. And now he was failing his duty toward his old love for this new passion and he was harried and distraught.

Moreover, he could see that all the days of work had not quite transformed Crystal Beach into a long deep sandy bathing shore. There was sand, but it had such vast rocky places to seep into!

Mamma was sorely tried. Privately she told me a million years wouldn't make that a sand beach and that Father was simply possessed. When we went swimming, she deliberately stepped on the rocks instead of the bits of sand. Father, of course, had no time to swim. He just waded in from the last unloading every day, got into dry clothes, ate supper, and fell into bed.

Mamma went ahead with her plans for the farewell tea, knowing Father would not attend and making the best of her cross.

She had lovely sandwiches with cucumber and chicken, and little deeply frosted cakes, and tea and coffee and mints. She hoped it would be a cold day so the tea could be served by the open fire, away from the full view of the bay and Father, but fate was against her.

She asked him to row in quietly and make no disturbance and come to the back of the cottage and slip in and dress quietly. She kept urging the need for quietness.

In the middle of the tea, Father came chugging down the bay. Remembering that Mamma was having guests on the porch, he had made a concession to looks. He wore his long underwear over instead of under his bathing suit, and had added a pair of brown gym shorts as a top layer of modesty.

As he hove in sight, sitting on top of the washtub which was brimmed with sand, conversation on the porch died.

Spellbound, everyone stood up to watch as Father neared the dock and the following boat came up and whacked the front one soundly. Father bent over and looked back, and at that moment the outboard motor, already discouraged by its past, unhooked itself and fell overboard in about eight feet of water.

Father was quick, he rose to his feet with a wild cry and flung himself toward the vanishing motor. But gravity was too much for him, the motor slid away out of sight as he hung upside down reaching for it.

"He's lost it," said Mamma, putting the teapot down with quiet desperation. Then she said, "Do have another cup of tea."

"No thank you, we'd rather go and watch," said the guests.

The tea party moved to the beach where Father's comments could be heard quite clearly. He stood up again in the boat, took off his hat and shipped the oars and then dove into the water. It seemed a long time before he reappeared, but finally he broke the surface of the water again, strangling. He held to the side of the boat and rested a moment and dove again.

"He can't lift it under water," said one of the men.

"He'll never find it!" said another.

Father's head rose again. He shook the water from his eyes. He was completely oblivious of his gallery. He seemed to be speaking to himself. Mamma and I knew what he was saying but his voice was tired and did not sound very loud.

He sank again.

"He'll drown!" whispered a lady guest.

Mamma began to scream. She was simply shouting at him to stop it this minute.

This time he broke water rather slowly, clung to the boat

a little longer, then dove again. This last time, he obviously came up with the motor for there was extra splashing and thrashing in the water, and then the motor slipped back again.

Father was past speaking now, he just held to the boat and breathed heavily, and the second boat swung slowly around and gave him a heavy blow in the rear. Father kicked at it rather feebly and it swung away again.

"You come in here!" Mamma was shouting.

But Father vanished. He was going down to the bottom again. Once more he came to the top, once more he had dragged the dead weight up by what stubborn strength nobody knew, but again the wretched thing slipped away, and plummeted downward.

By now the men were organizing to begin a rescue party, but as Father went down again, Mr. Cooper's trim little speed boat came putt-putting from the Cooper's shore. And when Father rose to the top, Mr. Cooper reached him.

Mr. Cooper presented some feasible argument about a chain or something so Father finally allowed Mr. Cooper to tow him inshore.

It is possible he would have kept on diving for that motor until he stayed down with it permanently, but he came trailing up the beach, still gasping from the struggle but very much alive.

"The confounded thing slipped," he said fiercely. "It slipped right out of my hands!"

The party was over.

Mr. Cooper helped him dredge it up the next day and take it to be rebuilt. And Mamma developed a bad toothache so that we had to leave immediately for home.

[51]

Father wanted her to pack the hole with cloves and wait a few more days so he could finish up his hauling.

Mamma said she couldn't stand it another minute. I knew what she meant, but Father didn't.

I went down with him to empty the spring box and he stood and surveyed his summer's labor. Around and between the stones, here and there, you could see the sand.

"It's all the fault of that confounded motor," he said, "I should have five more loads by now."

He went along the beach, heaved a few boulders from their natural resting places, moved them inshore.

"She never did have good teeth like my family," said Father. "Always running to a dentist."

But we went home, nevertheless, and all winter he talked about his sandy beach. You could see that he was still there in his heart, shoveling sand. And he suggested that we drive up as soon as the roads were open in spring just to "check things over."

We went up on a cold March day when snow still frosted the highways. The sky was brilliant and the air overlaid with spring. Father was in a hurry and cruised along at seventy which was unheard of for those days. I got carsick and Mamma was frightened, but we reached there at last.

The closed cottages were lost but lovely in the cold pale light. Pine needles had drifted up the steps and their scent was sweet. Mamma unlocked the door and stepped in the dim shuttered living room.

But Father bolted to the beach, and I ran after him.

He stood at the edge of the water looking down when I caught up with him, and black disbelief was in his eyes.

There was not a single grain of sand anywhere on the

whole stretch of beach. The wet rocks gleamed in the cold sun. Driftwood was scattered at the high water mark. An old rusted anchor rested near the dock.

But there was no sand anywhere.

Father just stood there looking, and his hands knotted into fists. All those boatloads of sand he had with infinite labor moved to his beach had been wiped away, of his summer's work was no least trace remaining.

He turned, at last, and trudged slowly back up the slope. I followed, not daring to say anything, because whatever I said would be wrong. My stomach was a tight knot and my throat ached. I just couldn't bear to have Father suffer defeat.

Mamma had the windows open, the shutters flung back. Timmie was chasing a squirrel in the backyard. Father paused at the edge of the path, and waited for me.

"Well," he said, "if we can warm the place up enough, we'll stay overnight. Then we'd have time to run over to Bailey's Harbor and dig up that Indian village."

"But, Papa, nobody even knows where it really is!"

"I do," said Father, "I figured it all out. The trouble is nobody has dug deep enough. Those state men were just lazy, that's all. That Indian village will have priceless relics in it. And we," predicted Father confidently, "shall find them!"

Squaring his shoulders, he stepped briskly up the steps.

"Grace," he called imperiously, "where's my compass and my good shovel? And what have you done with my high boots?"

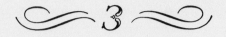

3

The Social Light

THE ONLY WAY I CAN ACCOUNT FOR FATHER BUYING THE LAND and building the cottages is that he didn't quite realize it would mean staying all summer in one place. He was excited over the building and the clearing of the land. He helped so hard on the cottages that the workmen privately told Mamma she ought to keep him away. He was too full of ideas for doing everything different.

Mamma was like me in her feeling for places. She was in love with the dark deep woods and the shining great water and the little Scandinavian village. When she was ill, in later years, she would say, "I'll be fine as soon as we get back to the cottage."

I loved it too. When time came to leave, I always slipped back down the cliff while Father racketed around loading the car, and laid my cheek against the brown clapboards by the back door and pressed my hands flat against them. The boards smelled resinous, they were faintly sticky around the nailheads. I could feel the beating heart of the cottage under my cheek and hands, sad and lonely now we were leaving. This was my love, my only love, this small house in the deep cedar woods, and most dreadful was the parting. It was years later that I realized everyone did not have this aching passion for a place, that Mamma and I were rather odd.

The place itself, and the life there, was typical of the era before the wars. There were good roads up the peninsula but no train or bus service, and nobody ever dreamed of plane trips. People who had no cars arrived on the Chicago boat which docked twice a week, bringing supplies, freight, and passengers. Mail came by car from Sturgeon Bay when the car didn't break down.

In the village there were no juke boxes, dance places or antique shops. There was an ice cream parlor with a marred upright piano in it. Sheet music like *Oh You Beautiful Doll* and *The Sheik of Araby* was displayed on the rack in case you felt like playing between banana splits and hot fudge sundaes. You could buy beaded moccasins and birch bark toy canoes shipped from a Chicago factory.

The sale of playing cards was forbidden. The only liquor dispensed was patent medicine. The inns, of which there were several, were run by the natives and at twelve-thirty when the big dinner bells tolled, people just sat down and ate tons of exquisite food with no cocktails to stimulate their appetite. It was possible to buy bottled beer in one store in Fish Creek down the line, and we all thought that settled the status of Fish Creek. It was *fast*.

Once a week a movie was shown in the old massive warehouse at the end of the big village dock. We sat on planks supported by barrels while the film wavered unevenly on a screen hung loosely from the cobwebby beams.

Most of the cottages had kerosene stoves, oil lamps and outhouses. Water was pumped by hand. The electricity in the village itself was produced in a small building near

[55]

the water's edge and it had a way of chunking along nicely for awhile, then stopping abruptly and plunging the whole village into darkness. It was all cut off at eleven-thirty anyway. The inns kept oil lamps which were more dependable.

I used to love to watch the lights in the village from our beach across the curve of the shore and to shout with sadistic pleasure, "The lights are out again!" Our Aladdin would be sending its warm lemon glow from the window.

The same summer people came year after year. They raised their children, and the children married and built cottages and raised their children there. They were rich and poor and the boats at anchor ranged from sea-going yachts to wobbly skiffs. But nobody bothered about wealth or poverty. This little place was American Democracy to the deep heart's core, maybe because the life was simple, maybe because the kind of people who loved it breathed something special in the pine-sweet air.

There was, however, some social life. Picnics and swimming parties and sailing parties. There were afternoon teas and little dinners served on porches overlooking the old serene bay. There were hikes and horseback rides, church suppers, and, at the summer's end, there was the regatta.

It was Heaven as far as Mamma was concerned. She loved picnics and she loved to float in the water in her heavy wool bathing suit, and she loved porch suppers, and she loved teas with the ladies sitting pleasantly together sewing and talking about their children.

But it was too tame for Father. He grew more restless every summer. After he had lugged all the boulders around and made concrete walks, cut down trees and dynamited stumps, tried to move the sand beach and fought with the Park superintendent, and made steps up the cliff and built a fishpool, he was ready to move on.

"Why don't we take a trip to northern Michigan?" he said. "It is fine country up there."

"It's better right here," said Mamma. "Why don't you take a day off and read the *National Geographic?*"

"I don't want to sit and rock all day," said Father.

Mamma felt she had taken trips enough with him before the cottage was built. We had gone constantly, and Mamma and I simply dreaded those little trips. Maybe we would have enjoyed them if we could have gone comfortably and really seen the great country.

But Father wanted to rough it, and rough it we did. Gadgets for motoring were not yet on the market, hotel accommodations were scarce and not always good, the day of the motel was far off. Roads were poorly marked or not marked at all. Most of them were detours.

But Father had fixed everything. He built two long black boxes the size of coffins and looking just like coffins which he screwed to the running boards of the big old Keeton he was driving. When they were in place, the only way to get in the car was to climb up and leap like a gazelle. One side of the car was sealed off permanently as that box was built up to the window. The boxes were made of the heaviest lumber, the biggest screws, the longest spikes, for Father liked things strong. They were padlocked with great locks; one of his phobias was that someone would steal something if he turned his back a minute.

On the car top went suitcases and more boxes, roped and lashed to withstand a hurricane. We never had hurricanes in Wisconsin, but one never could tell. Inside the car were layers and layers of bedding, pillows, raincoats, sweaters, knapsacks. This was topped with Father's shovel, his mining engineer's pick, camera equipment, and above all, up under the roof, the large Irish setter, Timmie, and me.

The tent was lashed on in back, and the tent pole ran the length of the car over everything else. Yards and yards of black mosquito netting fitted in around Mamma.

Pots and pans and kitchen untensils and canned goods filled the coffins. Father never expected to be able to buy anything after we left the home town. He was a frustrated explorer, equipped for either a safari or an Arctic trip whenever we traveled.

We always left around five in the morning for "We better make a good early start," Father would say, "or we'll never get anywhere."

By the time the car was loaded, the house closed, Mamma, Timmie and I settled, we were worn out. Mamma wore her long duster, goggles and a thick veil. Father wore his mining clothes, which gave him a rakish air. They were too heavy for these motor trips so after the first ten miles, he began to pull things off. I wore a middy suit, a duster, and a sailor hat.

We would drive like mad all day, whisking past all the pretty spots, avoiding the scenic places, because if we kept stopping all the time we never would get anywhere. Then we would pitch camp at night in some woodland rampant with mosquitoes, usually damp and cold to boot. All that carload had to be unpacked, the tent set up, the fire built, supper cooked, the pans washed, the food put back, the cots made up. About half past eight we sank into the canvas pallets and listened to the drone of the mosquitoes and the honk of strange wild things.

We never found a lovely camp site because we passed these before Father was ready to stop. We saw them, out of the back window, as we flew past. One I remember still was a little lost blue lake with a pebbly shingle, a row of clean pines, and a dry place for a tent.

"We can't stop here," said Father, "it's only five o'clock!"

At six in the morning Father would be briskly chopping firewood and urging us to get up and not waste the whole day. Mamma would stagger out, get breakfast while Father and I took down the tent and packed the boxes.

Timmie, meanwhile, would forage for a dead fish or some garbage. No matter how he came back, he had to sit on top of me as we bowled away.

We covered an immense territory on these pre-cottage trips, but mainly my memory is of flat tires, spiders in the bed, damp clothes and the half hour stops while Father filled the radiator. I was always thirsty, for Father was afraid of germs in the wells at the farms where he watered the car.

When we came home, Mamma and I were bitten, burned, exhausted. Father was fine. He could tell his best friend, the Doctor, how many miles a day we had made, what rock formations he had discovered. He had, it developed also seen the great bald eagle over the mountaintop, the wild duck nesting near camp, and a thousand other things we hadn't been able to see at all.

So when Father suggested a few trips during the summer, Mamma was adamant. She decided to encourage him to become more social, to settle into the summer colony life, hoping he might be entertained and satisfied. Besides, she thought he ought to make some gesture toward normal social life.

She began her campaign by buying him a pair of ice cream pants and what we called a sport jacket. She made him take one pair of good shoes to the cottage, too.

Father's shoes were a problem. He had sensitive, rather small, high arched feet and since he so rarely sat down, they took dreadful punishment. His feet were always hurting him. Finally he found a salesman, who said he understood Father's feet. He was a good salesman, and Father was enchanted. He bought pair after pair of the same shoes, and though they were obviously not right for his feet, he was happy with them. He kept a dozen pairs and hopped from one to the other several times a day. They were black shoes, coming well up over the ankles and laced part way with islets, part way with rows of hooks to snag the cotton laces over. They were hideous.

Once my uncle gave him a pair of elegant white summer oxfords, but Father wouldn't wear them. They looked silly, he said.

Early in the summer, Mamma invited all the neighbors for a beach supper. Father, dressed and brushed, would be relaxed and soothed, she was sure, and they would be off to a fine social season.

She had a little trouble with him over the picnic table on the beach. He decided it wasn't strong enough so he made a new one out of two by fours and heavy planks. He got it finished about fifteen minutes before the first guests came. So he had to hurry to clean up.

Mamma was busy in the kitchen. She had fried chicken

that night and a salad mold, hot biscuits, cherry preserve, oil pickles, coffee, and strawberry shortcake. Father was to make the coffee on the beach over a small open fire, and he had carried logs in all morning, and Mamma had busied me taking some of them off again for fear he would burn down the whole peninsula.

The guests arrived before Father. The men wore light summer suits and the women pretty colored prints or pastel linens. I wore my pink tissue gingham with the Irish lace collar, and Mamma had an organdy apron over her brown voile. Mamma's brown eyes were shining with excitement, for she dearly loved parties, and this was such a beautiful day! The curve of the shore was a pure white, the water deep blue as far as you could see. Finally it met the softer blue of the sky at the world's edge.

One of the Norwegian fishermen was out in the boat with the faded orange sail. The sail blew softly against the sky. Inshore someone in a dark green canoe was playing a tinny phonograph and the words came sweetly over the water.

As we went down to the table, Father burst out of the bedroom. He had the ice cream pants on all right, but an old torn shirt topped them. It was the first shirt he had found. He was too hot for the jacket, but he had his good lavender suspenders on, so he felt perfectly costumed.

He was curiously shy when a group first gathered, although this was a complete contradiction in his character, and he was blushing now and smiling with embarrassment as he greeted the guests. He looked so young and untouched at such a moment, his eyes bright, his cheeks flushed.

But he was himself again as soon as food was served.

Polite social chatter was never his métier, but he did not hear anyone say anything favorable about the Democrats, so he felt at ease now.

Until the talk turned to the college curriculum, that being the era of great change in educational requirements.

"Education is doomed," Father said clearly, "when you put in fly-by-night courses and give credit for them. Sociology," he said scornfully, "Education! Teaching you how to teach! Either you can teach or you can't, and that's the sum of it."

"But the modern trend," observed the economics professor.

"Greek," said Father, "Latin. The sciences. These are the basis of a decent education."

"But after all, Spanish is really a fine . . ." began the romance man.

"Pooh," said Father, "anyone can pick up Spanish with a book."

"But every man has an idea of the best subjects," ventured the Bible professor, "you can hardly leave out comparative religion."

"The really basic subject," said Father, "is geology. Without geology," he said, "where would man be?"

Mother was frantic. "Would you pass the cake, dear?" she asked hastily. Father helped himself and took up a position at the head of the table. Most of the men were red and angry, except the Greek and Latin men.

"Now take psychology," said Father pleasantly, turning to the psychology professor. "It's interesting enough. But not an exact science. In fact, Herbert, you know it shouldn't be classified as a science at all! A lot of theories, most of them pure hypotheses. Now it's absurd to give as much credit to a psychology major as to a physics major. I don't know what the world is coming to," he added gloomily, taking another piece of angel food.

"Who is going to the regatta?" asked Mamma, stepping on Father's foot.

"Ouch," he said. "Watch out!"

"I think everyone will be there," said a lawyer who didn't bother about curriculums. "I understand they're going to raffle off a new automobile."

"Gambling," said Father shortly. There was an uneasy silence. Mamma looked flushed. She had secretly bought three twenty-five cent tickets out of the grocery money.

"It's for the new church furnace," said Mrs. James.

Father opened his mouth and another battle was imminent. Then he looked past Mrs. James into the woods.

"Confound it," he said, and bolted to the cottage.

The back door slammed as he rushed out again.

"What's the matter?" cried Mrs. James.

Father reappeared around the corner of the house with his big ugly blue revolver in his hand. Mrs. James screamed. She had a phobia about guns anyway, and now she may have thought Father was going to shoot it out with her on the gambling question.

Father bolted past the party, vanished along the path. An instant later the gun went off with a loud report. Mrs. James sank down on a bench.

Before anyone else could move, Father came back, holding the big revolver in front of him with a pine snake dangling uncomfortably from the end of the thick barrel. He was grinning, relaxed, at peace with the world.

[63]

"Go away!" screamed Mamma.

"Just see what a fine specimen he is!" said Father.

The party went to pieces. Mrs. James was helped to the porch and restored with smelling salts and a cloth soaked in vinegar held to her forehead. Father went off happily with his snake, decided to burn it instead of burying it. He put it in the trash burner by the back door and poured a ginger ale bottle of kerosene over it, and the smell of burning snake billowed all over the place.

The gathering broke up rather abruptly, and as soon as the last good-bye had been said, Father sat down and unlaced his best shoes.

"Well," he said, "I thought they'd never go!"

Mamma was speechless. Rage really choked her. She put a hand to her forehead.

"Headache?" asked Father innocently, "I should think you would have. Enough to give anybody a headache standing around all afternoon doing nothing. Better take something for it."

Mamma found her voice. "You and your snake," she said. "You didn't have to disgrace us banging around with that snake!"

"He was after the wren's nest," said Father. "You want the wrens eaten up?"

"And arguing about everything," wailed Mamma. "Insulting half the guests! And then lugging that horrible snake right past the table!"

"Well," said Father stiffly, "I just want to say one thing! There isn't a man in that crowd could hit a snake in the head with one shot of a revolver at the distance I did. Some people would appreciate it."

"I know you're a fine shot," said Mamma, "but that doesn't mean people want pine snakes served with their tea!"

I slipped away to the beach. I was miserable. On one hand, I thought Father was simply wonderful to see that snake so far off and kill it with one shot. It was exciting and grand like *The Last of the Mohicans*. On the other hand, I knew Mamma's supper was ruined and the tale would go all over the peninsula. I stayed down quite awhile skipping polished stones and worrying about the way life was so difficult. Then I walked along the piny path toward Eagle Cliff, breathing the serene air.

When I came back, Father was at the end of the dock mixing up a batch of cement. "Got to reinforce the dock," he said.

Mamma was in the kitchen making dumplings for a second feast. She always comforted herself with cooking.

Father went off early the next day to help the Doctor work on his boat, and he was gone until late afternoon. I spent the day on a hike with a crowd of young people and got home just after he did.

"Set the table," said Mamma. "Supper's almost ready."

"I'm not very hungry," said Father.

This meant that his feelings were still hurt. He always felt that any loss of appetite on his part was a terrible punishment for the person who upset him.

Mother said nothing. She ladled out the stew, rich and savory with juices, and the dumplings, still light as a feather. Father had three helpings, and then he said, "I don't suppose there's any pie?"

"Cherry," said Mamma.

"Just a small piece for me," said Father, indicating that he had not forgiven her yet. But after the second piece of pie and three cups of hot coffee with cream and sugar, he felt better. He rolled up his sleeves and turned to Mamma.

"I will wash the dishes," he said. "You can rest."

This was a handsome apology from him and also his way of forgiving Mamma.

She went to the porch and sat down on the swing. It was hard to rest when Father did the dishes, but she tried. Father attacked the dishes and gave no quarter. He used scouring powder on the silver, sapolio on the best dishes, and once he went right through a weak aluminum pan with a cleaning pad. There was considerable breakage, too.

That night, as I wiped, he kept up a running conversation above the bang of pans and the spatter of hot suds.

"I've been thinking over your curriculum at college," he said. "Your first year will be Greek, Latin, mathematics and history."

"I want to take English," I said. "I am going to be a writer."

"Geology," he went on, "and botany you will need, and you might take some German later on. A good many fine scientific things are in German."

"I want to take English," I said. "I am going to be a writer."

"Well, you can read books, can't you?" he shot at me. "Anybody can read books."

"And I'll never pass mathematics," I said, with true prophecy.

"It's perfectly simple," Father scoured the inside of a

tea cup with cleanser. "You just put your mind on it. And when you get into astronomy, you will need it."

"But I don't want—" I knew very well I would take what Father decided, but I was going down with flags flying.

"The stars," he said, flipping the dishcloth in the air, "the stars—do you know how far away the nearest planet is?"

"No, Papa."

The next thing I knew we were out in the back yard and Father was giving me a lecture on the heavenly bodies, pointing with the carving knife. The figures passed by me in a blur, but when he began to dip into Greek legend and explain the firmament as the Greeks saw it, I was fascinated. Venus, Orion, Arcturus, Diana—the stories were lovely. From there, he nipped into early navigation and speculated on how the sky looked when Lief Erickson piloted his craft around the vast seas.

Mamma sneaked quietly into the kitchen and finished the dishes as Father began to quote Homer.

"The next time we go over to the Doctor's," he said, "remind me to show you his edition of the *Iliad*. It is fine. We might go over—what day is this?"

"Friday," I said.

"Friday?" he asked. "It seems to me there was something about Friday—oh, my gracious!" He darted into the house.

"Grace," he said abruptly, "I forgot to tell you! We were invited for dinner tonight at the Brinkley's."

"What?" Mamma dropped a plate.

"I met him in the post office yesterday," explained Father.

"You mean they were expecting us tonight?" Mamma was horrified.

"Yes, I guess so. It slipped my mind," said Father. "I remembered it when I spoke about the *Iliad* because—"

Mamma sat down. "We may as well sell the cottage," she said, "and move back to town."

"Now don't get excited," said Father. "They won't notice it. We can just explain."

"There are some things," said Mamma, "that cannot be explained." She added, "What time were we to go?"

"Seven-thirty," said Father, "because they had to meet the Sturgeon Bay train with her brother and sister-in-law from Chicago. We were supposed to meet them. I remember it all perfectly."

Mamma looked at the clock. Then she jumped up. "Get a clean shirt on," she said grimly, "and don't stop to fool around!"

We scrambled into our party clothes and flung ourselves up the cliff and Father drove like a maniac. Mamma said not a word, she was pale and controlled. We got there at five minutes to eight. As we pounded up the steps, Father muttered, "Party, party, party, day and night nothing but party."

"Hush," said Mamma fiercely. "You try to behave yourself, just for once!"

The Brinkleys were Chicago people, stocks and bonds, and they were greatly impressed by the fact that their cottage was built in the primeval wilderness. The relatives were timid, nervous people, scared of mosquitoes, frightened of wasps, and altogether out of their sphere.

The cottage was a heavy log affair, and they were in the midst of building a new foundation under the kitchen end, and they had considerable trouble excavating the rocky ledge.

Father got started talking about the age of that ledge, and launched happily into the prehistoric facts about the land. The whole Brinkley property, he said, had once been under a great sea, swarming with strange fish and mammoth sea serpents.

At this point the Brinkley colored maid bucketed into the room shrieking.

"A snake," she cried. "A snake under the stove!"

The Chicago relatives got up on their chairs. Mr. Brinkley shut the door to the kitchen. Mrs. Brinkley, who was timid as a bunny, was gasping for air.

"I want to go home!" wailed the maid. "I never said I'd work with rattlesnakes in my kitchen!"

The city folk were retreating to the front room. But nobody made a move toward the kitchen.

Father gave Mamma a look. "I'd be glad to dispose of him," he said, "but my wife doesn't like me to kill snakes at parties. I could come back in the morning."

Poor Mamma. Destiny was never on her side.

"I told you, Will, we shouldn't leave that foundation open!" cried Mrs. Brinkley.

"It's probably a nice garden snake," said Father easily. "The only poisonous snakes in this part of the state are the—"

Mamma turned to him. "You go out and kill that snake," she said in THAT TONE.

"You mean NOW?" Father was having a heavenly time. "Right at dinner?"

"Go on," said Mamma in a deadly voice.

Father skipped.

The male was vindicated, the female was wrong. He dispatched the snake with the stove poker, and came in casually saying, "Just an adder, that's all."

He was the hero of the hour. As we calmed down and dinner was served, he was discoursing amiably on the habits of snakes all over the world.

Mrs. Brinkley had roast beef, mashed potatoes, new peas, tomato salad and fresh cherry pie with ice cream. Mamma looked a little pale as she refused a second helping, and my own stomach, fortified by beef stew and dumplings an hour earlier, was not up to standard. Bitterly I regretted the second piece of pie I had eaten at home.

But Father was going happily along, eating and talking and basking in the admiration of the ladies. All in all, it was a memorable evening. Mamma looked pleased, although I could see she thought Father ought to let someone else say something now and then. Still, she must have felt he was making progress. For there was no doubt but that he held the attention of the dinner guests.

And then, as Father finished his cherry pie and reached for his coffee, Mrs. Brinkley, pie server poised, said, "Do have another piece of pie and some more ice cream."

"Thank you, no," said Father, smiling affably.

"Just a small tiny piece?" she urged.

"No," said Father, "I HAD supper just before we came."

There was an astonished silence.

"So I really am not as hungry as I might be," said Father and added with a bright smile, "We had cherry pie, too!"

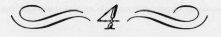

Money of Her Own

MISSIONARY SEASON CAME AROUND AS REGULARLY AS CHRIST-
mas. In those days, the missionaries traveled around from
church to church, giving talks to gather funds for the Lord's
work. Sometimes they were just in from Rangoon or Burma,
sometimes from Japan or China. Once a Reverend Mac-
Lean came from South Africa.

Sometimes, of course, they only came from the Chicago
Mission office, without glamour, wreathed in no glory.

Missionary season was always a time of unrest at our
house. Mamma loved the missionaries and would have
given them every cent we had, but Father felt differently.
I remember one particular struggle vividly.

"You keep away from those missionaries," he said. "All
they want is money. Take every red cent if they could."

"But, Rufus," said Mamma, "we have to do our duty
by the heathen! Think of those poor benighted souls with
nobody but the missionaries."

"Ha, ha," said Father, "they have their own governments.
Why don't Americans stay home and mind their own business?"

Mamma's color was high, her delicate skin flushed easily,
and she looked wonderfully young and pretty when she

was excited. "Don't you *care* whether they are saved or not?"

"Pass the potatoes," said Father, wth dignity. "I tell you, if I had to have my soul saved by that last specimen you dragged home for supper, I'd rather not *be* saved!"

Mamma set her lips. Both of them were too absorbed to notice I was drinking the vinegar left in the bottom of my salad plate. How good it was, salted and peppered and still flavored faintly with cucumber. Father said it would eat the lining out of my stomach, and Mamma said it wasn't ladylike to drink it, so I always had trouble over it.

"And I don't want you throwing away my money," said Father firmly. "I have contributed generously to the fund for repairing the pews and fixing up the organ, and that's enough."

"Father, may I have a quarter?" I asked.

He fished out his snap purse and handed me one. His bright blue eyes twinkled. "Make it go as far as possible," he said.

I always knew when I could get a little petty cash outside of my regular allowance of twenty-five cents a week. This was just the moment, for it gave Father a chance to show how really generous he was, but it was the principle of the thing he struggled for.

"Is there any more of the apple pie?" he asked.

Mamma cut a thick wedge. The ice cream went on top.

All that week the missionary struggle went on. Mamma would slip up to the church and listen breathlessly to the lectures, and I went with her. In the dim light of the church parlor, the pale thin spinster would talk a long time, and the minister would speak and pray, and the portable blackboard would be covered with figures showing how much money was needed.

Mamma and I would hurry home in the early dusk, arriving just before Father came home for supper.

"Mamma, I wish they'd tell us more about what it's like over there," I said.

"Yes," said Mamma, "I wish so too. I would like to know what it's like inside a pagoda."

Mamma had to get supper in a hurry, but Father never suffered during the days she went to church, for Mamma was an expert. There would be country fried potatoes crisping at the edges, rosy slices of ham baked in mustard sauce, spicy stewed tomatoes, and a quick cottage pudding with caramel sauce. Father would have enough to last until his bedtime snack.

This particular year, Mamma had managed to save a little here and there, the way a woman did in that era. Father paid the bills on the first of the month, and there were charge accounts for everything. If Mamma wanted anything, she could get it, and charge it, and then defend her purchase when the bills came in. She had to ask for cash for streetcar fares and for her Wednesday club dues. I actually was better off than she was financially for I had a quarter a week of my own, increased to fifty cents the last two years of high school.

But there was one chain store on Main Street where for cash you could get things for less, and Father found this out and gave Mamma some money to use for specials at this store.

Mamma was a genius at managing. She could buy the cheapest cuts of meat—and oh, how cheap they were then

—and turn out roasts as tender as sweet butter. A turnip was a challenge to her, and what she did with plain winter carrots I never have approximated. So Father ate on, unmindful of the small roll of dollar bills in Mamma's jewelry box.

"I am going to have something for the missionary fund," said Mamma to me. "I feel I must. But it isn't enough for my share."

I could see it troubled her, for she was as sunny and open as a daisy field by nature. But this missionary business was a deep obligation.

In her childhood, the family purse had two divisions and in one went a tenth of any money that came in, this was sacred to the church, and no matter how poor they were, this money was never touched.

And besides, I think she longed to have a contact with those faraway places she would never see.

For the silver tea on the last day of the drive, Mamma baked an angel food cake, and made little filled cookies, and the ladies of the missionary society said nobody could cook like Mamma, and they couldn't. I passed the cake basket and was able to save three pieces for myself.

And on the way home, Mamma bought a flank steak, on sale instead of a porterhouse, and slipped the saved dollar in her purse. Flank steak was a gift, and braised with vegetables the way Mamma fixed it, it was elegant.

After supper, Father went off to a faculty meeting and I went upstairs ostensibly to do my homework but really to read *Spinner in the Sun*. I heard the doorbell ring, and peered down the stairwell, and saw that our Polish neighbor, Mrs. Plinko, was there. The Plinkos lived at the bottom of the hill and the father worked in the mill. Since he stopped frequently at one of seventy-two saloons, Father thought little of him, and assumed the whole family was no good. "Weak people," he put it.

Mrs. Plinko was crying and had her black shawl over her head. Mamma let her in, and they went into Father's study and closed the door. I crept softly down the Brussels stair carpet and listened as hard as I could, but the door was too thick. When Mamma suddenly opened the door, I was knocked off my feet.

"Get me my pocketbook," she said.

She didn't even bother about my eavesdropping. I brought the brown velvet bag.

"Now go upstairs and do your homework," she said.

I went slowly enough to see her take the missionary money out of the inner pocket as she went back into the study.

I sank right down on my bed. Mamma was giving away all the money she had for the missionaries! It couldn't be, and yet it was! I sat there until I heard the front door close, and then I flew back down.

"Mamma! Mamma!" I cried. "You gave her the missionary money!"

Mamma said, pale and composed, "She had to have it."

She moved to the kitchen and put the kettle on for coffee, a sure sign that she was agitated beyond help.

"Mamma, what did she need it for?"

"No need to speak about it," she said, "but I only want you to remember that wine is a mocker, strong drink is raging."

"Oh," I said, "did they cut off the gas and water too this time?"

"Never mind," said Mamma. "But I must say I think the Lord didn't really mean for the sins of the fathers to be visited on the children. Get out the peanut butter if you want a sandwich."

"Are you going to tell Father?"

Mamma pushed her brown hair back and sat down. "There is no need to worry him."

The sign of her conflict was still on her set lips. What a dreadful choice, between the heathen and the Plinkos!

I knew as well as Mamma that there was no time to go through all the pinching and squeezing and saving again. The missionary fund would be collected, signed and sealed Sunday morning after a last sermon on *I am my brother's keeper.* And there would be no pale brown envelope with our name on it in the collection plate.

"Oh, Mamma, if you could only get some more money," I wailed. "If only Father would—"

Mamma drank her coffee hot and black. "There must be a way," she murmured. "There must be a way."

Father came home then, and said the refreshments after faculty meeting were no good, so he'd like something fit to eat.

Mamma scrambled eggs with onion and cheese the way he liked them late at night, poured more coffee, and cut fresh salt rising bread.

"This is more like it," said Father happily.

Then Mamma spoke firmly, "I want you" she said, "to change your mind about the missionary fund."

Father buttered his bread. "Change my mind? Why in the world should I do that when I know I'm right?"

"But you are not right," said Mamma, getting pink.

"I," said Father, "am not a silly sentimental woman."

"Even a man," said Mamma, "should have concern for God's work. A Christian man."

Father was getting red too. "That's right," he said, "accuse me of not being a Christian just because I won't throw away good hard-earned money for nothing!" He dished up more eggs for himself. "I" he said grandly, "have a family to support, and it's not thanks to you I am not bankrupt."

"The money you would give to the missionary fund," said Mamma, "would certainly not keep us from bankruptcy. Of that, I am sure."

"Father, may I have a quarter?" I asked.

He gave me a look, then handed out the quarter. Well, I could give that to Mamma, I thought, but even if they argued all night, I thought the prospects of getting another quarter were slim.

"Go on up to bed now," he said, "or you'll be late for school in the morning."

I could hear them as I braided my pigtails. Father got madder and madder, they were really going over the heathen and the missionaries thoroughly. And as they came upstairs Father was shouting, "Not one cent of my money. That's final."

He slammed around getting ready for bed, and Mamma went into the sewing room and I heard the foot pedal going. When she was really upset, she would sew feverishly far into the night, she wouldn't shout back at Father, but she had plenty of spirit and she wouldn't settle down meekly beside him while he snored if she was angry. She would merely stay up and sew, and that, I thought, made him simply wild.

"Aren't you ever coming to bed?"

"I have a little stitching to do."

"It's late. You better come to bed."

"After a while."

"You'll never get up in the morning if you don't get to bed at night."

"I am not sleepy."

"Don't blame me if you have a sick headache tomorrow."

"I won't," said Mamma sweetly, "but I thought I could mend my old underwear and give it to the missionary barrel. That would be something."

Father uttered a groan and said no more.

After a little, I got up and went in the sewing room. Mamma was sewing at a terrific pace, her hair was loose, her eyes were dark and bright.

"You ought to be asleep," she said.

"Mamma, why is Father so mean?" I burst out.

"He isn't mean." She stopped the treadle. "He is just convinced about things."

"Well," I said hotly, "if I ever get married, and I don't think I shall, my husband has got to give me five dollars a week even if I want to throw it in the garbage!"

"Oh, dear me," said Mamma, "who ever heard of such a thing?" Then she turned and gave a long, thoughtful look. Her face was pale now and her eyes wide.

"Money of my own," she said slowly, "that I had a right

to spend." She went into such deep thought that I moved away and went to bed. When she got one of her thinking spells, she never noticed anybody else until she was all through thinking.

The next morning we had waffles with crumbled maple sugar and melted butter, with tiny country sausage cakes on the side. Father came downstairs at peace with the world after a sound sleep and with waffles in sight. Mamma was deftly lifting a golden brown waffle to a hot plate. She wore her blue dress with the white collar and she, too, looked cool and serene.

Father kissed me. "Smells good," he said. "Hope you made plenty."

We all sat down and Mamma served the plates.

"I've about made up my mind to give you a new stove," said Father, helping himself to the brown curls of sugar. "I was talking to Will Bradford yesterday. Of course they are expensive, but they don't leak gas, and there's a thing keeps 'em from smoking everything up. How does that idea strike you?"

"I'd rather have the money," said Mamma.

"Money? What for?"

"I've decided it would be very nice to have a little money of my own," she said calmly.

Father stared at her, thunderstruck. If she had threatened to elope with the garbage collector, he wouldn't have been any more astounded.

Then he got red. "I suppose I don't provide well enough for you," he said stiffly. "I suppose you wish you had married Ed."

"Providing has nothing to do with it," said Mamma. "I

just want a little money to do what I want with. So I think I'll earn some."

"Earn money? You earn money?"

"That's what I thought," nodded Mamma.

Father laughed, suddenly relieved. "What a notion! You earn money? Just how did you think you would be able to earn any money?"

Mamma looked at him steadily, a strange little smile curving her mouth. "I am going to earn it," she said, "by cooking."

"Cooking!"

"People will buy whatever I make," she said calmly. "My things always go first at church sales."

Father choked.

"I shall take orders," said Mamma complacently. "It will be quite simple, really. I just never thought of it before."

Father stood up with awful dignity. "My wife," he said, "my wife out earning money! You must have lost your mind! Would you drag our name in the gutter? Earning money!"

"Everybody will understand," said Mamma. "There's no need for you to be upset."

"When I am dead and in my grave," said Father, "if you want to go around selling pies and cakes, nobody can stop you. But while I am still here, I must ask you not to pursue this mad idea further!"

And leaving one whole waffle untouched, Father made a fine exit.

Mamma said calmly, "You may finish his up if you like. He had just started it."

"Mamma, you didn't really mean it?"

"Never you mind. You go on to school." And she added, "You missed a chance for one of those quarters now."

I couldn't get over it. I could hardly wait to get home from school. But at noon, after I jumped from my bicycle and dashed in, I found my lunch on the table and a note from Mamma saying she was out.

"I have gone out," she wrote.

After school, I was held up for an extra rehearsal for the chorus for those who couldn't stay on key very well. Consequently, I didn't get home until nearly suppertime. I dashed in again.

Mamma had just come in. I knew this because she had on her Mother Hubbard and I could see her best brown silk skirt swishing under the apron hem. She also had on her good high-button shoes. Bacon was crisping in the iron spider, and she was slicing onions. Liver and bacon, I decided. We had been eating it a lot. It was cheap and Father liked it.

"You can set the table," said Mamma, over her shoulder. "I haven't had time. Father'll be in any minute."

She looked as calm and quiet as a June lake, but it was the same kind of quiet with which she took my temperature when I was sick.

I heard Father then, pounding up the steps, and I flew with a load of plates to the dining room. He hated to wait for anything, especially food.

The sun was just setting and a clear wash of gold came through the silk net curtains. Under the trees the light was darkly cool like still water. It was so peaceful at the twilight supper hour. Usually I played one of the new Hawaiian

[81]

records while I set the table, like *Moana Lua* or *Wailiana*. But tonight I didn't dare make a sound.

The air was already crackling.

"What's this I hear?" Father was shouting. "What's got into you?" He was just warming up.

Mamma's voice was so light and so cool. "Remember, dear," she said, "the neighbors have ears."

I crept to the door of the dining room and peered through. She was dipping slices of liver in flour, salt and pepper. Father was waving his arms and stamping.

"I want to know what you have been doing!" he roared.

"Why, what's the matter, dear?" Mamma faced him.

"It's all over town! All over town!"

"Oh," said Mamma, "you mean about the tearoom?"

"Tearoom!" He was gasping for breath.

"Nothing to get excited over," said Mamma, laying the liver neatly in the black spider. "It just occurred to me that Libby Jones has been trying to find a partner. Since Ben died, she's been wanting to turn her house into a tearoom. But she needed someone who can really cook."

She turned the gas down low. "You know I am a very good cook."

Father was a very dark red. His mouth was so tight the words were bitten as they came out. "If you have any idea I'll permit my wife to run a restaurant—"

"Tearoom," corrected Mamma.

"My wife running a dirty filthy restaurant—"

"A clean tearoom," said Mamma.

Father seemed to fill the whole room. A masterful man at his quietest, he was a whole army attacking now.

"Of course it's nothing to you whether you disgrace my

name or not," he said, "and drag your daughter's name in the dust. Going around behind my back trying to work in a restaurant."

"Tearoom," said Mamma.

"Tearoom be confounded," roared Father. It was a shame he was not a swearing man for this was the time for all the words in the book.

I was shaking so the doorknob rattled in my hand. Nothing like this had ever happened in the family circle before. Mamma crossed Father now and then, but not with this hard and open rebellion. She always tried to get around him, now she was openly defying him, and he knew it.

He went suddenly white.

"Grace," he said heavily, "you can either give up this notion or me. You can take your choice!"

Suddenly a whole rocket-burst of stars went off in my head. I pushed open the door and rushed in. "Mamma, you ought to leave him!" I cried wildly.

Father looked as if a rattlesnake had crossed the room. Whether he thought I sounded exactly like him or whether he realized the horrid truth that the females would stick together, I don't know.

"I'll divorce you both!" he shouted. "Both of you!"

Then he flung himself out of the door and vanished.

I sobbed. "Mamma, aren't you going after him?" I cried. "No," said Mamma.

Then we were both crying and Mamma got her smelling salts in the little dark green glass bottle with the silver stopper. We smelled and sneezed and smelled again. Then Mamma wiped her eyes and moved around putting the liver back in the warming oven and turning off the onions.

She was so strange I hardly knew her. So collected and calm and so white.

I thought the end of the world had come. How in the world could Mamma go around working at supper? I simply stood motionless with the smelling salts in my hand and my eyes hot with tears. Father had cast us out, it was all over.

Suddenly the door banged, and Father was back.

"Supper's ready," said Mamma calmly.

Father strode to the table and stood looking at her. And then he spoke. "Grace," he said, "if I give you fifty dollars for your missionaries will you stop all this nonsense about the restaurant?"

Mamma looked back at him, and the color was coming back to her cheeks.

There was a long moment of silence before she answered. "Why," she said softly, "that's very generous of you, dear."

"Will you?" he demanded.

Mamma turned the big spoon over in her little hand. "Of course I don't really want to go against you in anything," she said slowly. "So of course if you really wish—"

Father gave a heavy sigh. He reached for his wallet and pulled out some new crisp bills and laid them by the platter.

"There," he said, "there you are. I didn't realize you had your heart so set on those—those confounded missionaries."

And then they forgot me completely for Mamma went right into his arms and he kissed her, not just a good morning peck but quite, quite differently. So much so that I felt a sudden dreadful pang of loneliness. I was left out.

But Father saw me and swung me over into his arms and

kissed me too. Mamma was smiling and her hairnet was entirely demolished so her soft brown hair was flying around her face.

"Oh, my dear," she said, "all the souls you have helped to save will bless your name!"

"I'll thank them to mind their own business," said Father. "When I need my name blessed, I'll take it up with God myself."

He looked at the stove. "Supper about ready?" he asked.

"In one minute," said Mama. She reached over and picked up the bills and tucked them into the teapot on the shelf.

"And I hope you're satisfied now," said Father.

Mamma began to dish up. I hurried to finish the table. By now it was dark and I took a chance on lighting the candles. Mamma and I did love to eat by candlelight, but Father liked to see what he was eating.

Father was able to eat three helpings of liver and onions, without reference to the candlelight. He ate two pieces of Boston cream pie. His only comment was, "We haven't had a tenderloin for some time."

"We can have one tomorrow," promised Mamma.

She wouldn't be pinching for the missionary fund any more, I thought, and life would be peaceful again—as peaceful, that is, as our life ever was.

Father was gentle as a dove. He gave me a quarter voluntarily after the table was cleared, and offered to do the dishes. We could hear the sound of his battle in the kitchen as Mamma turned up my blue corduroy jumper.

When he was through, he came in and got me to play

for him while he sang, *"How dear to my heart are the scenes of my childhood, when fond recollection presents them to view"* and *"I hear you calling me"*.

He finished with the old Welsh special air, *"Love Lies Bleeding"*.

Then I went up to do my homework and skipped through it rapidly. I had too much to think about to worry over Caesar's troubles. I went to the window and stood looking out at the stars drifting the darkness of the sky. Would those heathen ever know, I wondered, what our family had gone through on their account? No, they never would. How many souls would Father's hard given money really save? Fifty dollars was a fortune!

And would Father give fifty dollars next year when the missionaries came back? This I doubted.

Then I pondered whether God would credit this gift to Father when He knew why Father had given it? That the money was just to keep Mamma from working in a tearoom, not because Father yearned to save the heathen.

I was still standing there when Mamma came upstairs and said, "You better go to bed, dear."

The starlight fell on her face and she was beautiful.

Father was banging away downstairs in the usual shutting up routine. Mamma moved over to stand beside me and look out at the loveliness of night.

"What a beautiful world," she said. "And how thankful we should be for all our blessings!"

"Mamma, is everything all right?" I asked.

"Everything is just fine," said Mamma, and put her arm around me. A star fell, blazing down the deep sky.

[86]

"Father wouldn't really divorce us, would he?" I whispered.

"No," said Mamma. "No. I don't think he ever would." She pushed back her hair, and smiling, bent to kiss me goodnight. "Father is a wonderful man," she said.

She turned back to the door, and said, half to herself, "Still it would really be great fun to have a tearoom!"

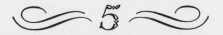

Father's Romance

CLEANING THE ATTIC WAS A REGULAR AUTUMNAL OCCUPA-
tion. Attics are gone too. There may be a big cobwebby
place under the roof, but more likely it is rented to a
young couple who keep house with a hot plate. The first
war cleared out the warm old clothes, usable blankets, and
the second war cleared out everything but the rafters.

It is a minor sadness to think of the old taffetas and silk
gowns given away, the old letters added to the waste paper
drive, the piles of books and magazines shipped away. Even
the dolls like my own Flora Dora with the long brown
curls, were added to the boxes for war children.

The romantic attic is no more, and brave would be the
woman who began again to tuck the little baby shoes and
the love letters away under the eaves. It is not that kind of
world any more.

In our attic we had old sea chests filled with albums and
letters, there were trunks of velvet and satin dresses with
long tight bodices and full skirts, any one of which I might
wear today. There was a file of *Little Folks* and of *St.
Nicholas* magazines and of the *National Geographic* complete since the first issue.

There was a wondrous hair wreath in a walnut frame.
There was a baby bonnet which had framed the golden

curls of my dead baby sister, and a long flannel petticoat embroidered heavily which were the baby brother's.

But to me, the pictures, the old fading albums, the photograph books were the real treasure of the attic, and while Mamma cleaned and sorted, I hung over them.

Father was a beautiful young man. Sitting in the attic, looking through the albums, I studied his pictures. There he was, standing beside his racing bicycle, one hand spread tastefully over his tight coat and one resting on the narrow handlebars. The bicycle had one wheel twice as high as Father, and one wheel no bigger than a butter plate.

He was slender, short, his hair very curly, his nose very straight and decisive. His mouth was extremely sensitive in the early photographs, and the lower lip stayed softly curved as long as he lived, but the upper thinned down from his habit of pressing it in a hard line. As the more rigorous part of his personality won out, the mouth tightened, zipped close. He grew, in fact, to look more and more like the steel engraving of the first Mather, and, except for the clothes, might have posed as the first of the line, the upright and godly minister who calmed the sea in 1672 by speaking to God about it. Thus the ship landed safely in the New World—all because God paid attention to this ancestor, and that this was true, we all knew. He had said so in his diary.

There was the picture of Father next, with the Johns Hopkins hockey team, but it was so fogged I could hardly make out his small figure behind the long curved stick. There was a story that he was the fastest man on the team, and when they went to Canada he was close to becoming a professional hockey player. Knowing Father, I couldn't

imagine anyone faster. Also they said he skated like a madman and was always ready to whang his stick on the skull
of any enemy player. This, too, I can believe.

Mamma had seen one game and nearly fainted. Afterward she told Father he could stop that murderous sport
or never call for her again.

How she managed to prevail on him was never made
clear. But he did actually give up hockey. It might have
happened at the time he broke his nose for the third time,
I don't know.

Opposite the hockey team was Father with his violin.
His face dreamy and soulful, he held the bow drawn as if
he were making the sweetest music ever heard. It didn't
seem strange to me at all that the violin and the hockey
stick were associated, for I had known Father ever since I
could remember.

He had earned his way through college by singing and
playing the violin. At the same time, he kept his scholastic
record at the very peak, made Sigma Xi, the scientific honor
fraternity, and was a charter member of Phi Delta Theta.
He was also the only man in the class to climb the greased
flagpole and drag down, or put up, the banner.

In short, Father had a full life.

Really it was small wonder that he had no patience with
students who made less than A simply because they happened to be on the football team. Father thought they
wasted a lot of their time standing around in the halls talking to pretty girls. If they kept their minds on their studies,
they would have no trouble.

He never had much sympathy with men who had to work
for their tuition either. He felt the best men worked their

way through anyway, and he had a basic distrust of students whose fathers paid their way through college. It was a little weak, he thought.

I knew all these things well, because my own life was a grim battle to do as well as Father had when he was in school.

I did not quite inherit his steel constitution, but I spent an awful lot of time leaping about the basketball floor, whacking tennis balls against the side of the house to improve my stroke, and even puffing in last in school relay races—for Father also, alas, had been able to race.

I did my best about the music, too, but since I couldn't just pick up the violin and play it readily, Father decided I had no ear and refused to let me take lessons. I took piano, always longing to take violin.

For the entire course of my schooling, I trembled if I had less than an A on my report card, and this worked out very well except for mathematics. I never could do mathematics and Father looked down on me considerably in consequence. He felt I simply did not put my mind on it, it was perfectly easy.

One day in the attic, I came upon a small secret drawer in the black sea chest, where the old sailor had kept his special treasures. There were pictures in it, and there I came upon the portrait of Louise.

"Who's this girl?" I asked Mamma.

Mamma pushed back her dust cap and looked.

"That was Louise," she said.

"Another aunt?"

"No," said Mamma, getting pink. "That was your father's first girl."

"You mean Father had another girl?" I was astounded.

Mamma dusted the *Grand Canyon At Sunset.* "He **was** engaged to her," she said, briefly.

Not another word would she say. The girl in the portrait **was** beautiful, I could see that, she had long curls over her shoulders and big soft eyes and an elegant watered silk gown which revealed very smooth shoulders and one of those popular swanlike necks. Mamma had almost no neck at all, not enough even to wear a high collar.

Father was engaged to this girl! Who was not my mother! My heart began to pound like a pestle. If Father had married her, where would I be? Would I not be at all? Would I be me, just the same? No, I couldn't, for I wouldn't have inherited Mamma's chin and hands and feet, or her swift sense of humor either, for that I never could have gotten from Father.

I faced the terrible mystery of life all at once in the shadowy attic.

And I had to find out about Louise.

It took a long time too. I asked Father about her, and he flushed to his ears and said, "Louise was my girl."

"But what happened?"

Being engaged in that time was as good as being married—at least as final. Once plighted, everything was finished. People did not go about being engaged here and there, and if Father and Louise were engaged, how in the world did it happen that Mamma was mending his long underwear now?

"What happened?" I insisted.

He grinned sheepishly and sent me out for an errand.

"Did she die?" I asked as soon as I got back. I could be **stubborn** too.

"Certainly not," he snapped. "She was perfectly healthy."

"Then what was the matter?"

"She didn't do right," said Father, and that finished it.

Mamma was a softer subject for investigation.

"He got mad at her," she said, at last, under constant persecution. "I don't think it was much in the beginning. She kept him waiting or something. But they quarreled, and he said she would have to ask him to forgive her. He would never go to her first. And Louise," said Mamma, "was a high-spirited girl. She wouldn't ask him. She never did, and he never saw her again."

"I guess Father didn't care very much," I said uncomfortably.

"He was very much in love with her," said Mamma. "It was his pride."

How much violence and passion lay in that old story! Father's pride I knew all about, and his necessity to be right. Then I tried to imagine what it would feel like to give him up. Especially after you had announced the engagement!

How Louise must have watched down the elm-shaded country road for the first sight of that great racing bicycle! How she must have read and reread the poems he had written her from college, those sentimental Victorian poems about true love!

And as the days passed, how she must have wept in the night, and sponged her face with vinegar and water in the morning. But she had her own high pride, you could even see it in the old picture in the lift of her head and the way her eyes looked out.

And Father went back to college without a word spoken between them.

It was after pursuing the subject of Father and Louise as far as I could, that I began to consider Mamma as the girl he did marry. I asked a lot of questions about Mamma's girlhood, I pieced together gaps in the story, I gradually saw her not as a parent, but as a girl Father chose after the unfortunate episode of Louise ended.

Poor Louise. I daresay she married a man easy to get along with, equable and unromantic and stable. And I daresay she dreamed of Father for a long time.

Then came Mamma.

She was beautiful too, with her shining dark eyes and soft dark hair and demure sweet mouth, but she was softer, gentler. Mamma never worried too much about her pride.

The best picture of her showed her in skating costume, with a muff held under her chin. She was an elegant skater, and sliding over the black river ice was her favorite sport. She was graceful, light on her feet, and had a straight slender figure.

Mamma could not carry a tune, or play any instrument, but she could draw and paint water colors with a charming innocent style. She was as feminine as any woman could be, and Father might have thought she was a clinging vine, if he stopped to think at all.

Mamma was an oak, but you had to know her to guess it.

At the time of Father's blighted romance, his brother, Ned, was courting Mamma. There were eight in the family, four boys, four girls, and Father was away at college, but seven were at home. Mamma was enchanted by the gaiety, the volatile high spirits, the careless living that went on in the great old farmhouse by the Connecticut river. There was music all day long, there was incessant eating, there was a constant flow of conversation. For amusement they went skating, tobogganing in winter, driving or riding in summer. The boys fished and hunted, the girls arranged costume parties and picnics.

Everybody did exactly as they pleased as far as Grandmother could manage. Grandfather did not permit card playing nor dancing, nor any activity on Sunday beyond church and hymn singing. But some of the hymns were pretty lively by Sunday afternoon.

Ned was a tall quiet boy who was destined to take over the farm and let it run down because he had no talent for farming. He was a victim of the times, for if he had chosen his own career, he would have done well. He could sing beautifully. Father and Fred were the tenors, Ned and Lisha sang bass and baritone. The girls divided up nicely into high soprano, contralto and mezzo. Anybody not singing could always play the piano or violin or any instrument anyone had left around. Grandmother and the youngest daughter played the organ.

Mamma's own household was a quiet one, and she adored this family. Things progressed rapidly to the point where she was included in all the activities, and Ned was calling for her regularly.

I do not know the exact day that Father came home, but it was probably during the spring vacation. Mamma never made it clear. But she was at the homestead with Ned. Therefore the family must have been gathered around the big old grand piano. Mamma would have sat on the green velvet sofa in the light of the green stained glass lamp.

Suddenly there was a flurry and a quick stamping of feet and Lida, the sister who loved him most, gave a cry and rushed to the front door and there stood Father, cheeks red with wind and excitement, eyes bluer than any blue in the world, hat clapped crookedly on his tawny curls.

Mamma, coming from her own restrained family, must have been dazed at the kissing and hugging that went on as they greeted the flower of the family back from the portals of learning.

And then, standing with his feet a little apart, and looking critically at Ned's girl, Father probably just said, "I've heard who you are."

And Mamma probably answered with spirit, "Anyone hears about you whether they wish to or not."

Father dashed off to the dining room for a snack of baked beans, brown bread, pickles, hot coffee, and apple pie, after which he felt a little stronger and unpacked his violin and moved into his place by the piano.

He played awhile, and then sang with Lida accompanying him.

He sang *The Lass with the Delicate Air,* and he looked at Mamma. He sang right through to the end, which was unusual for anyone in that family. They were always deciding to change the key in the middle of the page, or stopping to argue about the correct tempo. Also they always preferred to render something they did not know, rather than perform a familiar number. The minute they mastered a piece, it was dull.

But this time Father finished the last note without a single stop.

[96]

It couldn't have been more than a week later that Mamma had her surprise.

Ned came to call, and sat uneasily on the horsehair sofa in the small parlor. He was awkward and flushed, and his mouth was wistful. He wore his best blue suit and a shirt with a high starched collar, very formal.

"I only came," he said, "to say . . ." He hemmed and hawed and cleared his throat, "I only came to say I won't be calling again."

Mamma went pale. What had she done? Had she skated too long with the Pierce boy? Had his feelings been hurt because she said right out that the minister was dull? Or was he—was he tired of her company?

"Why not?" she asked. She couldn't help being direct, but her voice faltered.

"Well," he said, with a sigh, "we talked it over. Rufus wants to call on you himself, and it is only fair when he is away so much of the time. It is only fair—" He ended in a burst of speed. "I promised to give you up!"

Mamma was speechless. But after a few minutes, she found plenty of words. "Do you mean to say you two think you can pass me back and forth like a—like a sack of potatoes?" she demanded.

She stood up and faced him. "And what have I to say in the matter?"

Ned said, "Well, I don't feel I should stand in his way. He said if you had promised me—but when it seems to mean . . ."

Mamma sensibly burst into tears. For she couldn't ask Ned if he loved her, she wasn't in any position to insist that he continue to court her if he decided not to! And as for Rufus—

"I don't want to see either of you again, ever!" she cried, and flung open the door.

When he had gone, Mamma thought it all over. Here she had been going so comfortably with Ned and having a fine time and now without so much as a by-your-leave, this high-and-mighty brother turned up and dictated everything!

Just because he went to college, he thought he could manage everything! Of course she knew Ned was in no position to ask the hand of any girl. He was working for his father on the farm. On the other hand, Rufus hadn't a red cent either, he was still in college. He would graduate in June and then have to start out to earn a living!

Mamma knew all about the cost of living for her own father had died of tuberculosis—galloping consumption —when she was four, and her older brother worked in a grocery store to support the family. So she was not an affluent young lady. She had tried to teach school in a little one-room schoolhouse sixty miles away, and been so home-sick she had given up after four weeks.

Teaching was the only career genteel enough for a lady, and when that failed, she was just another young woman at home.

Mamma was going over all this in her mind, working herself into a fever. She was furious at the two boys, angry about the whole situation, and helpless to do anything at all! On top of everything else, she knew that Father had been engaged before, and the engagement had been broken off mysteriously. There was a good deal of talk about what had happened.

No, Mamma decided, he simply did not want his dear brother throwing himself away on a penniless girl. That was it, she thought, holding a wet cloth to her forehead.

The next thing she knew, the brass knocker roared against the front door. She was alone in the house, so she had to answer. She pushed her hair back, mopped her eyes and went hastily to the front hall.

"Good evening," said Father blithely. "I came to take you for a drive."

Mamma stared at him. There he was, so much like Ned and yet so very unlike. Ned was quiet, unaggressive, shy. Father had an imperious dynamic air—almost it was as if Ned were a water color, Mamma thought, a portrait in clear colors, and Father the copperplate for an etching.

Father was just tall enough to look down at her, he bent that shining blue gaze on her dark troubled eyes, his mouth smiled.

"Hurry up," he said. "We ought to get to the top of the hill for sunset."

He was an army with banners, and the sound of golden trumpets, and wind in tall pines, and thunder at midnight.

Mamma looked up. A man hard and ruthless and sure— and a woman's life would never be easy, never be serene.

"Come along," he said, impatiently. "Get your bonnet."

They were married in June, while the ink was still freshly black on Father's parchment.

Ned was best man at the wedding.

Father, at least, had no qualms. Everything had gone exactly as it should, that is, as he wanted it to. There was no reason to suppose it would not always be so. They drove away in the handsome buggy with Dolly trotting nicely along.

The sun shone, the sky was blue, the Mohawk trail shimmering with green shadow and golden sunlight. Father handled the reins expertly, his beautiful young wife was tucked in beside him (and she had also been just what his brother wanted, which made it even better).

The old Indian trail made a pleasant road along the hills, and the honeymoon trip was all the way from Pittsfield to Springfield.

And Father had a job too. He was going to work for the government on a geological survey in Maryland. He was happy.

Mamma may have felt the qualms. The only time she had been away from home before was that ill-fated teaching episode when she was way off beyond West Springfield. Now she was going off to travel all around the country, live in one boarding house after another, and never know from one hour to the next what her young husband might decide to undertake.

And while seventy-five dollars a month was an ample amount for two to live on, she knew it would cost a lot to board or rent rooms. Also, Father's job was not a permanent one, and while he had no fear about that, she did.

She may have wiped a few tears from her eyes with that lacy handkerchief now laid away in the haircloth trunk. But love was going to make everything rosy, they would be happy surely.

This was the dream, and now Father would turn and speak the words to her which would illumine the way.

They were alone, and the honeymoon was beginning, and now he would speak.

He did. He jerked the buggy to a stop, bounded out suddenly, called back, "I'll be just a minute!" And he leaped up the side of the cliff.

Mamma sat and held the reins and waited. Twenty minutes later, he puffed back, his wedding suit brambled and dusted, and a few hunks of rock in his hands. "Wonderful specimens," he said joyously, laying them beside his Gladstone bag.

Then he hopped in and they rode along while he explained all about the specimens, how they came to be formed, and how they got on that particular cliff.

Mamma admired his knowledge, but she couldn't help wishing the conversation were more personal. He might at least mention the wedding or her dress or her bonnet.

But around the next bend, he was out again, investigating the bank of the cold mountain brook. He found lovely glacial scratches and a handful of migrant pebbles.

Mamma had no interest in the pre-glacial period. But she was to spend her life intimately involved with it, so it may have been a good thing that the honeymoon drive was only a leap from specimen to specimen.

When they reached their destination, Father lugged all the rocks in for fear someone would steal them in the night. Mamma still looked like a bride, but Father looked like a prospector.

Sex had not reared its ugly head in that time, and for Father the word never was to be mentioned. He would have burned the mildest magazine article on sex education for children or incompatibility in marriage, the kind of thing children now cut their teeth on. He had a kind of deliberate innocence about what we call the 'facts of life.' After I was grown and married, a near neighbor became pregnant in the natural way and spent a lot of time in the late months sewing with Mamma. Everyone expected she would have twins, for obvious reasons, but when the baby arrived and Mamma said to Father, "Nina has a little baby girl!" He said in surprise, "Why nobody told me she was going to have a baby!"

Mamma was reserved, but a woman of deep and profound feeling. Father was too vital and too intensely masculine not to be a passionate man underneath all the delicate conventions of the day.

Nobody could ever really know about the first few days of that marriage, for Mamma never spoke of such things to her dying day, and since sex was not in Father's vocabulary, his love life was never destined to be mentioned.

It is just as well he never knew about the college courses ultimately to be given in education for marriage. If I had ever taken one he would have turned me out of the house.

The honeymoon was a typical Victorian affair, therefore, with the exception that whatever vapors Mamma may have undergone, Father never noticed them. He never for one instant put himself into anybody else's place, for he was much too busy being himself.

Then, too, he had won his bride. She belonged to him and there was no question of his ever losing her, under any circumstances whatsoever until death did them part.

He was not troubled by any worries as to making marriage a success or making it work or any other such fol-derol. They were married, they were on their honeymoon, and as he dumped the rocks by the walnut commode in the first country hotel they stayed at, he was indulging in no introspection of any sort.

He gathered Mamma into his arms and kissed her and crushed her wedding bonnet and tore her new silk hair net to pieces, and as soon as she could draw breath again into her crushed lungs, he must have suggested that it was suppertime and how about a nice steak?

And no matter how loving he may have been in the night, and how much Mamma may have been persuaded that she was really his whole life, I know that around six-thirty in the morning, Father was racketing about, flinging up shades, knocking over the water pitcher and saying, "Wake up! We can't waste all day! It's time to get up!"

Mamma's job as a personal valet began immediately. She had never visioned herself as a handy house servant, but that was her new destiny. Father never picked up a sock, folded a coat, or put anything in a drawer in his life. So I know the first morning Mamma was pouring his hot water and laying out his clean underwear, while Father shaved and cut his tender skin and said, "Confound it, this razor's no earthly use."

No breakfast in bed either, while they talked happily of the wonderful future ahead. Downstairs they went, to the dining room, completely accoutered for the day and ready to eat and dash off like a firehorse.

Father was inclined to worry if he were too comfortable lest it be some streak of laziness creeping out. Yet he loved luxury, so you never knew which feeling was going to be uppermost at any given moment.

They had a light breakfast of oatmeal and cream, sausages and pancakes, and possibly a plate of fresh doughnuts with their coffee, and then, whisk, they were on the road again.

"It's already after eight o'clock," Father snapped the reins. "We should have been on the way half an hour ago!"

They were bound for Baltimore, and at the end of the buggy trip, a friend drove the buggy back home, and they went on by train.

Baltimore seemed as far away as Indo-China to Mamma. But Father loved to be on the way somewhere, anywhere. The buggy ride had been all right, but the train went faster. He roamed the coach, tried to get a ride with the engineer, almost got left behind at a station where the train stopped to take on water and he dashed off for specimens. Years later, he did get a ride in a cab, but not on this trip.

Tired and homesick and draggled, Mamma followed him into the Baltimore station. They took a streetcar to the boarding house corner, and then climbed the stairs to their first home. The little rented back room was dark and not very clean. Father dipped his head in the washbowl and shook the drops from his curls.

"Well, here we are," he said confidently. "Let's go out now and look around!"

If Mamma had any romantic notion of being carried across the threshold, she got over it. She combed her hair, washed her face and dusted it with rice powder, put on clean white cotton gloves, and was ready.

"Hang onto your purse," said Father, "you can't trust these Southern people!"

He was sublimely happy. He loved strange streets, strange faces. Mamma stepped carefully after him, never quite keeping up with his rapid stride, and wishing she were at home on the nice sidewalk by her own house. The brick pavements were uneven, the air was hot and close, there were people speaking in a foreign tongue everywhere. She couldn't understand them, and nobody could understand her either, as she soon found out.

She was a little Yankee alien.

Father was perfectly at home. That night in the boarding house, he took out his violin and played for all the guests, and sang all the favorite songs. A pretty young school-teacher from Alexandria played for him, and he laughed and joked with her while they performed. Mamma sat with her hands folded in her lap, her heart beating heavily under her lace corsetcover.

Standing in the greenish gaslight, Father looked young and gay. He sang *The Lass with the Delicate Air* and then he sang the song which was her own song, and he looked at her as he sang it.

> *"In my garden grows a blossom,*
> *Love lies bleeding is its name*
> *And my neighbor's pretty daughter,*
> *Came and set my heart aflame."*

His clear high voice rose in the still dusky air like a golden fire, and his eyes, in the greenish light were bluer than star sapphires.

The ladies whispered and fluttered and waved their silk fans, and Mamma pressed her small thumbs together and adored this strange and wonderful being.

Ah, who shall say when a romance ends? How many times in the dull or bitter hours of a lifetime comes again the echo of a lost song, the scent of a faded rose? Father, who lived in the moment and lived it to the hilt, was little given to remembrance of things past. But he too, now and then, could remember.

I know he could, for sometimes he made me pick out the notes for him as he sang *Love Lies Bleeding*.

He remembered then the boarding houses, all the boarding houses, and his young bride sitting on the hard sofas, the slim and gentle dark-eyed girl who left the familiar world she knew to follow his wandering stars.

But the actual end of the romance, perhaps the end of this period, was the day of the river trip.

It would do Mamma good, he said, to go out with him on the survey. Fresh air and exercise, she needed them. He was dredging up fossils in the river bed, on the basis of which he later proved something or other about the age of the river formations.

He chose the hottest day of all, the air steamed, the sky was a burning stovelid. Mamma might have preferred a small stroll in a leafy park, a cooling ice in the late afternoon, and a chance to finish the embroidered lunch cloth she was making against the day when they might have a home.

"You come with me," said Father. "It will do you good!" Mamma tripped along, never knowing she would spend thousands of hours on all sorts of expeditions. She sat by artesian wells, she waited for oil to seep up, she perched on cliffs much of her time. But she was as yet innocent, and she went trustingly.

He had a small and rather leaky rowboat for the trip and

Mamma was settled precariously in the rear, protected from the burning sun inadequately by a big white straw hat and a parasol. Her skin was even more sensitive than Father's, so she wore long white gloves. And a lace scarf over her shoulders to protect her neck from sunburn.

The river was glassy, the air scalding. Father rowed with zeal, making the little craft bound over the water. "It'll be cool away from shore," he said.

There was a lot of shipping in the river, a few becalmed sailboats, some smoky barges, a few freighters, and all the busy port boats. Father pointed them out and named the type of craft and Mamma squinted dutifully and tried to see them against the copper sun. But it was awfully hot and it did not get cooler farther out. They rowed and rowed downstream for what seemed eternity. Finally they landed in a muddy sludge around a bend and Father dug up buckets of river silt and muck and dumped them in the boat.

His face glistened with sweat and his shirt was soaked. But he was excited and happy. It was, he said, wonderful mud. Full of fossils. Mamma fended off gnats and flies as best she could and wiped her damp face. She privately thought nobody had ever dug so much mud before and never would again.

Then Father pushed the boat off, rowed awhile longer, and shoveled again. He had gunnysacks full of oozing, smelly treasures. The slimy leakage sloshed over Mamma's nice slippers. The sun blazed. Mamma had a sick headache.

"Couldn't we go home?" she asked.

"I want to go just a little farther down," said Father.

"I might find something better around the bend." He looked up. "What's the matter? Isn't it nice out here on the water?"

Mamma said nothing. She dipped her handkerchief in the muddy river water and tried to cool her forehead. She tilted the parasol hopelessly. The sun came in all directions.

"You better go up front," said Father finally, "to even up the boat."

He moved his sacks to the rear and sat on the back seat himself while Mamma slipped and skidded, crushing a few irreplaceable fossils as she did so. She wedged herself in the bow of the boat where it was even hotter and more uncomfortable.

Finally Father couldn't get another shovelful of mud in, so he shifted to the center seat, took up the oars and started back upriver.

They were a long, long way from home, and a little hot wind rose and blew against them. The load of shelly mud and rock debris made the boat heavy and sluggish. Father stopped and tied his handkerchief around his neck, pushed his limp Panama back on his head, rolled up his shirtsleeves.

And he rowed.

They moved, slowly and with difficulty, up the river. After an hour or so, Father was tired, and he was hot, and he was hungry.

"I could get there faster," he said, "if I didn't have your weight to hold me back."

Mamma got redder than her sunburn. "I didn't want to come," she pointed out.

"Well," he said irritably, "I don't get much thanks for taking you for a nice trip on the river."

They were drawing near a large steamer of some sort, though afterward neither of them was able to describe it accurately. But it was large, and they were near it, and it was pulling along to pass them.

"Look out!" cried Mamma. "Don't go so near!"

"They'll have to get out of my way," said Father fiercely, disregarding the size of his craft. "No business crowding in on me so." He looked up, and then he saw a long anchor chain dragging down behind the steamer.

"Look!" he said. "You see that chain there?"

"Yes," said Mamma. "Do watch out!"

Father bent to the oars and almost snapped them. "Now when I say so," he said, "you grab that chain, and hitch it through the ring up there! We'll ride home!"

"Oh, what will they say?" Mamma was timid.

"They'll never know the difference," he said, with more truth than he knew, "Come on now, watch sharp—grab it when I say!"

The rowboat spun wildly toward the big craft.

"Now!" cried Father, "catch it!"

Mamma reached out and by some miracle grabbed the swinging end of the cable and brought it aboard, covering herself with rusty water as she did so.

"Give it a double turn through the ring," he ordered, and shipped his oars happily.

Mamma managed some kind of hitch. Her hands were red and scratched and she bent over to wipe them off. "I don't think we ought to do this," she said, looking nervously up at the dark bulk so close to them, "I don't think . . ."

"Now you see," said Father, "we'll be there in a jiffy!"

At this point there was a sudden sound of engines. The steamer was getting up speed. It had been plowing along lazily, but now the captain had signaled full speed ahead, and the whistle blew as the water foamed under the bow. The boat swung into midstream and sped along.

Mamma screamed.

Well she might. The slight rowboat, pulled into the wake of the big craft suddenly stood on end. Mamma was high in the air, Father and his gunnysacks were almost submerged. At a frightful speed the little shell shot along, upended, much as a surfboard goes behind a speed boat. Father was suddenly hidden by a wall of flying spray and there was so much noise that Mamma, clinging for dear life to the seat, couldn't even hear what he was shouting.

One moment they were almost sucked under the black hull, and the next they flailed wildly back in the wake.

Mamma had never learned to swim.

Father was shouting and Mamma was screaming and still they spun along, upended with water swamping the boat, the oars swinging crazily. And Father's prediction that no one would notice was well founded on fact, for nobody did. The big boat steamed ahead and Father and his bride came ricocheting after.

Mamma closed her eyes and prayed. Father was yelling like a banshee. "Unloose that chain! Unloose that chain!" he shouted hoarsely.

Mamma finally heard him, but with all that pull on the chain, no human being could have unhitched it. Mamma, high in the air, cast a last despairing glance at Father down in the welter of water and spray.

And at that point, just as the little boat dove down into an oily swell for the last time, several small motor boats came whipping past, and in all of them people were standing up and waving their arms and shouting.

On the nearest riverbank, too, men were running along and shouting.

The captain of the steamer was curious, and he gave the order to slow down, until he could ask what was going on.

The rowboat gave a long shudder, rose again, the fateful chain slackened, the wall of spray diminished. Faces lined the rail of the steamer, faces blank with unbelief. The captain came and peered over, and all the motor boats scurried up. The engines stopped and the two boats rolled in the swell.

Father crept forward on his knees and managed to untie the hitch so the chain fell clear. The captain was swearing and shouting, and Mamma was sobbing.

Finally the young couple were set ashore safe, if not quite sound. The belated steamer and the furious captain were moving on upstream. Mamma had lost her hat and parasol and her dress was ruined, and she was already turning a mottled red with her sunburn. Father was a mixture of shells and mud, his shirt half gone, his pants torn.

They climbed on the streetcar and rode along to the boarding house. Mamma was still shaking with fright, hardly daring to believe they were alive.

She was already for Father's abject apologies and remorse as she climbed the dark stairs and reached their room. As soon as they were alone, she faced him expectantly.

Father flung down the gunnysacks which he had clung to insistently.

"Well," he said, "that steamship company ought to be sued! Endangering people's lives like that!"

Mamma sank on the bed and waited for the apology.

"They ought to be sued," he repeated, tossing his shirt on the floor.

"But they didn't . . ." Mamma began.

Father faced her. "And besides," he said, "if you'd been a little faster with that chain, it never would have happened!"

At this point, definitely, the honeymoon was over.

The Wonders of the Visible World

WHEN THE GOVERNMENT JOB WAS FINISHED, MAMMA PACKED the already worn suitcases. The wandering years were ahead, Father was ready to move on to new fields, new excitements. Mamma hated to leave the friends they had made, but he loved to know new and different people.

Two Quaker sisters were their closest friends. Quiet, gentle women in their soft Quaker garb, they opened their home to the young Northerners. There were delicious dinners served in the elegant old dining room in the high brick house, long evenings by the coal fire in the marble fireplace, and now from that vanished time a single sentence remains.

"Rufus, thee never played out half thy baby days," said Fanny.

Mamma cried and kissed them good-bye and promised never to forget them. And she never did. She wrote them regularly all down the years, and always sent Father's love. When they died, they left a silver service to commemorate the friendship. Father was considerably surprised, he had almost forgotten them, but Mamma knew better.

Father was well qualified to teach, and several teaching positions followed the survey. Somewhere in his career he taught Greek in a country school in Maine. He was slight and younger-looking than some of the pupils, and it was a tough school. The previous teacher had been driven out by the students.

So the first day, Father beat up the largest and most violent boy, who was twice Father's size but not nearly as fast. Thereafter, Greek was respected in that school.

Then there was the period in which he taught at the Colorado School of Mines, geology this time. In summer, he worked in the Portland Gold Mine, swinging a pick as a regular miner. There is a story there, of the young Professor who worked beside the hard-bitten miners born to the tunnels, but it is a story he never told me.

He loved the deep dark mine, the candle in his cap, the hard physical labor. The men were all right, he thought, except they used dreadful language. Father heard a good many new words, but he never adopted any of them. He stuck to "confound it." He learned in this period much of the practical knowledge about mining that he used later as an expert on gold and silver mines. When he wanted to know anything, he went right out and found out all anybody else knew about it. It seemed simple and direct, and it was.

Mining was pretty hazardous in those days, and Mamma was frightened. Every time he came home, grimy and black in his work clothes, she knew a brief thankfulness.

The first baby was a girl. Father had been too busy to pay much attention to the impending arrival, but when he saw the baby, he fell in love. This was his great love. As much as he ever loved anyone, he adored this delicate golden-haired child with eyes as blue and brilliant as his own.

The business of naming the baby established that.

Mamma had given it a great deal of thought. As a direct descendent of Cotton Mather, a family name should be chosen. On the other hand, her own family was just as early American, and this small baby had a very fine ancestor on the maternal side buried in Copp's Hill in Boston.

Added to this was the fact that children "named after" someone in Mamma's family, received a legacy from the Grandmother. The distaff names possible included Anner, Sibyl, Harriete, Fannie, Grace and Alice.

Mamma broached the subject when Father came in one night.

"I don't like those names," he said flatly. "They are terrible names."

He lifted the baby up and buried his face in the soft golden fuzz at the back of her neck. The baby's rosebud hands waved at him, Father said, "She knows me! See that? She knows me!"

"Well, the legacy would be nice," said Mamma.

"We'll not starve without it," he said, just as if he had a lot of money.

"I suppose you want to call her Minnie or Ida," said Mamma.

Father was rocking his arms, his cheek on the baby. "No," he said. "I don't like them either."

"Well, my goodness," said Mamma helplessly, "if she isn't named after a single relative, what do you want to call her?"

"She's not going to be named after any relative." he said. "She's going to be named something that fits her. She'll be named," he said decisively, "Majel, after Majella. It means wood dove."

"But that's just a name in *Ramona*," said Mamma doubt-fully. "It doesn't sound like an ordinary name."

"It's beautiful." Father closed the discussion. Mamma may have had something to do with the baby being born, but it was his baby now.

And so the baby was baptized in the Methodist church. Her name was Majel.

Father wrote a number of poems to Majel, his wood dove. He used to walk the floor with her and sing until she slept. He roused from the weariest sleep to pick her up and walk and sing. Poor as they were, he hired a man to do a colored painting of her and framed it in a gilt frame a foot wide. The face was exquisite, even a hack painter could not spoil its beauty.

The story was soon told. The family Bible opens easily at the first page and the words are a little blotted with tears.

Majel, born February 18, 1898. Died August 11, 1899.

They called it cholera infantum, but it may have been any one of a number of things. Babies, even passionately loved babies, died quickly, and no wild broken words could make them live again.

Father never really forgave God.

When the minister talked to him about God's will, Father said some terrible things about God.

And he paid little attention when the next baby came along, for he would not again give his heart to the hawk. Mamma could name her any old name she chose. It didn't matter. Mamma, worn with grief and child-bearing, didn't bother too much either. There was no poetry about this thing. Majel was dead. And God and Father weren't on speaking terms.

Mamma named this second child Gladys Leonae, and no poems were written.

The Leonae was a faint concession to the family, for there was Uncle Leonidas who had been an officer in the Civil War.

I was taken to see him one time, in the Old Soldiers' Home. I remember the hot still sunlight and the clipped sweet grass on the wide lawn, and the veranda with all the old men rocking on it. I remember Uncle Lonnie in his uniform. He had fiercely twirling moustaches and a very military stamp when he walked. His wooden leg made a heavy thump on the painted veranda floor. He smelled of tobacco and wool when he kissed me. The moustaches were scratchy.

But I had the wars confused, and for a long time I thought Uncle Lonnie was a Revolutionary soldier and had beaten the British.

The third baby, a boy, was born on a cool autumn morning a year after the second one, and he was named Walter, after Mamma's brother. For her, the dark-eyed laughing little boy was sun, moon, and all the heavens too.

He lived to be two years old.

Mamma bore her grief quietly, but twenty years later, time had not made it an old sorrow. In her heart she never got over it.

When I grew old enough to wonder about life and death, I spent a lot of time under the syringa bush in our back yard puzzling over why it was that Father lost Majel and

Mamma lost Walter, and the middle child, less than either of them, was left to grow up. Sometimes I wondered whether they had loved the dead babies too much, and God didn't like it.

Or maybe they were too perfect to live in this world. Whereas I was just a very ordinary child, neither beautiful nor exciting.

About the most you could say of me was that I insisted on living. I had all the things children could have in those pre-specialist days, including brain fever, but I simply would not die.

I would be given up regularly, but I always opened my eyes after awhile and swallowed the beef broth.

There were no more children. When it was time for Walter to be born, Father went off on a hunting trip, leaving Mamma alone with the help of a neighbor. And possibly at that point, Mamma decided she was through having babies.

After I was old enough to run around and play games, Father accepted me as the best they had left.

He gave me a wonderful gift. He gave me his childhood.

It was a continued bedtime story. The lonely thin little child, the solitary that I was, at bedtime became magically a part of that family of eight bouncing children. I really lived, not in the little flat or small cottage we happened to be renting, but in the great old farmhouse by the wide Connecticut river. The pond, the fields, the woods, the cattle and horses and chickens and rabbits and dogs, these were all mine.

Father's flawless memory brought it all back. I knew the top floor of the old house where the four boys slept. I loved the pillow fights which were so violent the plaster cracked on the ceiling below.

The four girls slept on the second floor and I knew where each one was. The great master bedroom in front was Grandmother's, and whoever had measles or mumps slept in the little room next.

The boys hunted and fished and swam. They were treed by bulls, they had circuses, they put snakes and frogs in the girls' beds, fell through the ice in winter, shot holes in the bedroom walls, and generally led a fine life.

And I led it with them. How I loved the time Father and Ned chopped out the poison ivy around the swimming hole. They wore their bathing suits and armed themselves with hatchets and chopped half the day.

"I guess this will fix it," Father said.

It did. Father spent the next two days lying in the bathtub, swelled beyond recognition. Grandmother put arsenate of lead, or something like it, in the water. Ned, who hadn't chopped so fiercely, came off much better.

"But we licked the ivy," said Father proudly.

Grandfather had a big dairy herd, and the boys ran the milk route and earned money for their musical instruments. They had printed milk tickets for the route, yellow and blue for quarts and pints and orange for thick cream. Father drove the wagon and coped with the tickets, and made quite a thing out of it.

There was no heat on that vast third floor, and it was not easy to bound out of the feather bed at four in the morning. You had to blow on your fingers before you could lace the heavy boots, and pull on the thick woolen clothes. Father would harness old Daisy to the white milk wagon as the hired man lifted the milk in. Daisy's breath foamed in the icy air, and Father tucked a hot brick under his boots as he started off down the silvery country road.

I, too, drove Daisy over the snowy New England roads, my mittened hands filled with milk tickets, my feet on the hot brick. Lying in my small cot in the Colorado night, I slapped imaginary reins on Daisy's neck, and heard the wagon wheels creak on the tight snow.

Long later, visiting at Grandfather's, I was poking around the attic with a couple of cousins. I found the milk tickets, piles of them, smooth blue and yellow and orange pasteboard cards.

"What in the world are those for?" asked a cousin.

"These are our milk tickets," I said impatiently. "Don't you remember when we had the milk route?"

Father took my hand and led me to his schoolhouse, the little red brick one room building in the meadow. All grades were accommodated there, and there was one schoolteacher.

The curriculum was not planned for enjoyment. Reading and writing and arithmetic were drilled into reluctant heads. There was a fat iron stove for heat in winter, a woodbox for the boys to fill, there were hard wooden seats, and a table with a tin water bucket and a communal dipper. The teacher sat in front with a blackboard behind her. She had a plain wooden desk and a straight chair.

The wraps were hung on hooks near the door, rubbers and overshoes went below, pinned together with clothespins.

There were no pictures except an unhappy engraving

of Lincoln, and there was no decoration to make school attractive. School was not supposed to be fun, it was a duty, and no nonsense about it. But through the small-paned single windows one could see the woods and the meadow, starred with violets in spring and sweet with the brook flowing. There were nut trees in the woods, and there was a nearby orchard in view, where the boys stole snow apples, crisp and sweet.

Many a good birching was given the four boys when they were dipping girls' pigtails in inkpots, or throwing wads of paper across the room. But much of the time, Father was looking dreamily out of the window, planning a hunt for frogs, or a foray after honey in the next farmer's yard.

If you ran fast enough, you could insert a thick stick in the hive, get away, dash back again when the bees had quieted, jerk the stick out, run again, and sit down with a great golden blob of honey to eat.

The bee men never liked this, it made the bees nervous. But they didn't have to catch you if you were fast enough. Father was.

Or he would think about guns. Next to musical instruments, guns were the best wonder of all. The boys could all shoot well, one of them grew up to be a champion shot, with medals and silver and ribbons to display on the parlor table.

But Father could hit a can thrown in the air, and drill it spang in the center. He could hit the bull's eye at an impossible distance. He also shot through the parlor window of the next house.

At night they practised loading and unloading and peppered the walls with casual shots. Grandmother didn't mind as long as they didn't shoot through the floor and hit one of the girls. She was a tolerant woman.

No clubs, no organizations, no recreation groups were available to those boys, and they had a wonderful time.

No day was dull. When Father shot the skunk, Grandmother put a washtub in the yard, stripped him and doused him. He buried his clothes by the rosebush and wore Ned's overalls. He had to eat alone in the kitchen for a few days.

"But it's not a bad smell," he said, "once you get used to it. You know they make ladies' perfume from it—like musk. Now musk comes from the musk ox, and he lives far away in a wild country which I will tell you about."

So we wandered with the musk ox for an evening and then came back to the time Father broke his nose the first time. Most children broke something now and then, but Father not only broke his nose once but three times. He fell out of a high tree climbing after a bird's nest. They didn't, of course, take any x-rays. The old family Doctor came trotting up in his buggy to stop the bleeding with a pack, and Father went about his business shortly. Then he broke his nose again playing hockey, and the third time he broke it in college. His nose, thereafter, had a slight slant, like a sail against a wind.

A broken rib didn't amount to much, and for a split head Grandmother threaded a firm needle and sewed it up herself. Father split his falling out of the icehouse onto the ladder.

Grandmother forbade him to go there again, but he went anyway. Tall and dim and cool with shadows, the icehouse was heavenly in the hot summer days. The ice was packed in huge chunks in sawdust, and the wet sawdust smelled rich and cool. You could dig down and chip off long slivers of ice and suck them, spitting out the twigs and frozen leaves. And you could see, from the high window, the silver blue pond where the heron had her nest and the young fawn came down to drink.

Snake killing was a very wonderful treat. When the boys had nothing special to do, they could always go in the swamps and kill snakes. If Father did not always get the biggest and fiercest, he thought he had. The technique of snake killing which I learned then, has been invaluable.

You have to be quick, Father said. You go along in the low places where the ooze is warm, and you do better at noon when the snakes come out to drink. If you have no gun, a rake is the best weapon. Bring it down like a lash, just behind the head. Never break his back, said Father, a snake lives at both ends.

For snake bites, drink whiskey. And burn out the bite with a hot poker, or cut across it deeply twice with a clean knife blade.

Whiskey was kept in the medicine closet off the dining room. It was never a drink, it was a medicine. It stood next to the Collygog and the Smith Brothers Cough Drops. It was used for chills and fever. And for snake bite. Or in case of fainting, a tablespoonful was poured into the victim's mouth.

A rattlesnake, Father said, gives plenty of warning. An adder or a copperhead may slip up on you. A water moccasin is not a good snake. A duck-headed adder is no good either. But green garden snakes are mild little fellows and eat insects.

Never yell when you see a snake, you scare him and he may get away, said Father.

A great python is a marvelous snake. Pythons and cobras live in the jungles in some parts of the world.

A jungle is like this— The jungle grew in the room, strange swaying vines, wild crying of scarlet and jade and turquoise birds, the slow prowl of a lion, tawny as an autumn cornfield. Elephants danced in the white moonlight in a clearing, crocodiles slid in the cinnamon colored mud by the rivers, mysterious flowers filled the air with a heavy lush scent.

Leaving the jungle, we slipped back to Grandmother's house, and were lined up for the sulphur and molasses for spring tonic. Grandmother got the bottle from the medicine closet and ladled it out to all eight children.

The medicine closet was a narrow room with a green and gold stained glass window which filtered colored light on the shelves of pills and bottles. There was a patent medicine for every ailment known to mortal man. Most of them tasted delicious and a hasty sip or two of this or that did no harm. Father grew up believing that it was a good thing to take plenty of medicine of different kinds, for if one did not work, another might!

Castor oil was the standard, and this was not pleasant at all. Father's faith in it never dimmed, and I took it all my childhood, always throwing it up as soon as I swallowed it, and taking it all over again. Father gave it to me in orange juice, and in black coffee, and in cocoa. It was years before I was able to keep any of them down even without the thick oil floating in them. Castor oil was administered for headache, sore throat, upset stomach, cold in the chest, and fever.

It was fortunate that the family had good strong appendices.

Grandmother used goosegrease for grippe, bronchitis or pneumonia. She rubbed it in the chest well, laid on a hot flannel cloth. For toothache she massaged ground cloves in the gum. And for any uncertain pain or ache, ginger tea was a fine medication.

Blood suckers were in their heyday then, but Grandmother did not like the long rubbery things, so bloodletting was seldom indulged in. The boys got some bloodletting in the course of swimming in the meadow pond, but the girls simply went unbled.

The medicine closet was always full, for the patent medicine men came around in their wagons regularly. They had Indian Remedies, compounded from mysterious herbs by Great Chiefs. They had Miracle Cures and Lydia Pinkham's Vegetable Compound. They had ointments of snake oil and herb teas and cherry bark cough medicine—called elegantly an Expectorant. They had horehound drops, and the Smith Brothers black gobbets.

Dosed with such a variety, it was no wonder the children were healthy as weeds. The smaller ones were treated with asafoetida for colic, and paregoric for teething. The older ones had rhinitis and aconite for colds and fever. The boys liked aconite, it came in small glassy pills that tasted like candy.

Grandfather was a firm, vigorous, but just man. He was one of the founders of the Congregational Church in the town, and on Sunday, dressed in a black suit and with high black leather shoes, he herded his eight lively children into the family pew.

Grandmother played the organ, so she was not responsible for their behavior during the two hour sermon. The four little girls and the four little boys and Grandfather took up a whole pew, and the oldest child, a fair, quiet girl, helped keep the smallest ones in some sort of order.

After church they drove home in the big old black carriage, and had a large formal dinner.

Then, stuffed with chicken and dumplings and mashed potatoes and gravy and vegetables in season and pie and ice cream—oh, to lick the dasher again with fresh peach ice cream thick on the paddles!—the boys were turned out to keep quiet and behave themselves. They could take off the copper-toed boots, hang up the tight jackets, and go outdoors.

They could not play any games, nor sing anything except hymns. They could not read, except the Bible or the Sunday School leaflet, which was a dull little sheet. They could take walks, but they could not swim. They could not skate or slide in winter. They were supposed to remember the Sabbath Day and keep it holy.

Grandfather rested in the afternoon, reading the Bible. Grandmother rested too, or played hymns. She did not cast an eye at her mending basket, piled with eight children's casualties in socks and pants.

The greatest day of emancipation was when Grandfather decided that possibly it was all right to look at the bound volumes of Stoddard's Lectures which were in the library.

Late in the afternoon, Grandfather might take a walk

himself with a span of boys at his heels. His broad green
acres, rich river bottom land were a comfort to look at. The
big barns were freshly painted, the fences in repair, the
cattle sleek and clean. The orchards were trimmed and cul-
tivated. Grandfather must have had his dream that these
fruitful acres would sustain his children and his children's
children forever. He would leave plenty of land, he would
leave money to maintain it. A careful farmer, a far-seeing
business man, he invested ably, bought a seat on the
stock exchange and laid away a good, though modest, fortune.

The boys who did not take to farming could go into the
paper business. Several of the relatives were already pros-
pering in the fine paper mills, and it was a family tradition
to "work up" in one or more of them.

It was a good time, and destiny was kind to Grandfather,
for he died with the dream unspoiled. None of the boys had
the heart of farmers, the land was sold off gradually to pay
bills, the barns sagged down. The fine herd of cattle was
dissipated, the chickens gave up laying and were eaten. The
gracious old homestead became a tourist house, the lavish
rose garden was tangled with weeds. Only the row of great
giant hydrangeas remained year after year lifting their
plumed rosy blooms in front of the old house.

The quiet river road was widened for through motor
traffic, and dust and oil overlaid the valley. But Grandfather
never knew it.

The backlog of stocks and bonds eroded away too. Except
for Father's portion. Father never sold anything. The one
time he ever parted with anything was years later when he
sold his automobile to a friend. A week later, he made the

man sell the automobile back to him. He had changed his mind.

The storytelling days were ended when Grandfather died. He died in a manner befitting his family. The cow barn was in need of repair and some men were working to replace the timbers. Grandfather went out to inspect the work, and found one corner of the barn sagging a little where a beam had rotted away.

"I'll hold it up," he said. "while you get a new timber in there."

"You can't lift up the barn!" said one of the men.

"I don't have to," he said, "I'm only going to hold up this corner a minute."

And hold it up he did, and suffered a stroke then and there.

When the news came, Father packed his Gladstone bag and started East. When he came back, we were at the station to meet him and as he got off the train, he saw us standing by the baggage truck, and burst into tears. The tears fell down his face, streaking the soot in long runnels, and I was frightened. I had never seen him cry, and his face was strange and pale.

We went home silently, and Mamma got out the coffee pot. Father stood looking around the little room as if he had never seen it before. His eyes rested on his violin on top of the worn upright piano. He moved across the room, picked it up, laid it in the case lined with faded blue velvet. He shut the case and locked it and carried it to the coat closet by the door. He put the violin in the closet and shut the door.

He never played a note on it again. Mamma carried it all

over the country up and down and back and forth, and finally gave it away secretly to some niece or nephew.

When I went to bed, I said hopefully, "Tell me a story, Papa."

He shook his head. "I'll read to you out of a book," he said.

He had put away his childhood, too, and when he finally got around to storytelling again, he made up the adventures of Daisy and Johnnie.

Father had grown a moustache to look older, but he looked a good deal older still after that trip East to the family cemetery. The cemetery lay in the green valley near the wide river, and the whole cemetery was filled with our family. There had been at least eighty relatives at the funeral, they made a large group standing among the old and new headstones. The sisters had showed Father the plot reserved for him and his family. Mamma was to be permitted there, too, since she had his name. Although they really did not like outsiders there.

Father had stayed long enough to order a white marble stone for Majel instead of the little marker. It had to be the whitest and finest marble in the world. Father was a granite man, but for the little lost wood dove granite was too rough, too severe. The soft marble was installed, and a grey granite stone set for Walter.

There was plenty of room left in the plot, Father said. But of course, he never expected to die himself. Father never had the faintest intimation of mortality in his life.

Maybe it was the loosening of the family ties that made him restless. At any rate, we moved again. We moved all over, and I could not say when we were in California and when we were in New Mexico and when we went to Old Mexico.

When people asked me where I lived, I always said, "I live on a train."

I remember the places. In California, Father set up his little family in a tent in Tent City. We went swimming every day. I floated in the salt greenish water beside him keeping up by clinging with one hand to his shoulder. I was too young to swim, but I could go anywhere with Father doing the breast stroke powerfully beside me.

We bought oranges in washtubs at twenty-five cents a tub. This impressed me because Father and Mamma kept marveling at it. The New England Christmas orange was a long way from this.

Cooking was sketchy. We bought food at a delicatessen, and I thought store potato salad in a cardboard box was simply wonderful.

But the best was walking the beach with Father. Every shell was a mystery and a story. The seaweed was a book in itself, as Father talked about it. I gathered the long cool rubbery strands, filled my pockets with sand dollars and small pale shells and struggled after Father's rapid steps. It's possible he was out of a job, for we must have been poorer than usual, but my world was furnished richly with the gifts of the sea.

Even the grains of sand were wonderful, for Father could sift out the shining grains and talk about the time they were rocks and what happened to them in the long sweep of centuries.

The stars overhead had their romance, too. Everything visible to man's eye was a marvel. The great tides moved by the moon excited Father, so did the track of a small greenish snail on wet sand.

We had a little old leather book written by that early member of the family, now known as a witch burner. On the faded yellowing pages the title stood out, *The Wonders of the Invisible World,* by Cotton Mather.

He had been a storyteller too, and he took his four-year-old daughter on his knee and described hell so vividly to her that she had convulsions. Father, fortunately for me, was preoccupied with the wonders of the visible world, and took no stock in anything you could not perceive directly.

When we packed up to move that time, I kept a small candy box of sea treasures, the pearl-lined, the silvery, the pinkish. The waferlike sand dollar was there, and the starfish, and Father let me keep a small bit of kelp too.

The New Mexico period was a milestone. We lived in a little adobe house in a small village, named Socora, or something like that. Father was teaching again, at the School of Mines.

Here was a home, if it were only made of mud blocks. Mamma wrote back to New England, and the boxes and trunks arrived. The wedding silver was unpacked, the good china. There were rugs to walk on, and they felt lovely to slippered feet. Mamma bustled. The painting of Majel covered half of the parlor wall, there was a sofa too, and real chairs to sit in.

One room was entirely filled with specimens and books. Father had made a collection of sulphide minerals for the Paris Exposition, and a large bronze medal was on the table by the papers. Most of the books were property of the French Government, lent him for his study. I was not allowed to touch a single specimen or lay hand on the price-less irreplacable volumes. I could rub my palm softly over the medal and wonder about the lady in flowing garments holding a torch. A man was flying through the air and she sat on his middle with nothing to hold either of them up. He also had strength enough left to wave a garland of laurel.

A special evidence of prosperity was the Carom board, which stood against the parlor wall because there was no other place for it. It was varnished and painted for checkers on one side, and it had little red silk net pockets at every corner. Neither Mamma nor Father ever played Caroms or checkers or any such game, and Father didn't like me to play Parchesi since you had to shake dice for it and dice were instruments of the devil. I used to lie on my stomach with the board before me and make up games, pushing the round red and black counters over the highly polished sur-face. Someone must have given the board to Father, for this small game of mine certainly did not justify such an expen-sive and large board.

Father had a black horse and rode to work, dressed almost like a cow puncher. The horse was named Raylampego, meaning lightning, and he was just that. Mamma said Father was extravagant for he paid a thousand dollars for him. He probably paid a few hundred after due bargaining. He was always known as the thousand-dollar horse, how-ever.

I had a burro named Nellie and, for the first time in my life, a playmate, a little Mexican boy who lived next door. We conversed with gestures until I learned enough Mexi-can Spanish to chatter at him.

We both used to ride Nellie around and around the

house, for she wouldn't go anywhere else, and when she had enough of the ride, she went under a low tree and scraped us off in the red dust. Once when I offered her an apple, she took my hand with it and bit me rather severely.

And one day Father came riding home with a baby lamb under each arm. He found them dying on the desert after the flock had gone on, and lifted the thin dirty bodies in his arms and galloped home. Dusk was coming and the yard was shadowy.

I was on the narrow stoop watching for him, and the horse was high and black against the pale sky as he came riding down the road. The little limp black legs hung on either side of the saddle, Father's face was excited.

"What in the world have you got now?" asked Mamma.

"Lambs," said Father. "They aren't quite dead."

Mamma dug up a nursing bottle and we all took turns holding it while they frantically sucked in warm milk. Father carried water from the well, heated it, and made a washtub full of warm soapy water and we washed them. They came out whiter and softer than a new snowfall. Nobody ever was as rich as I was that night.

They followed me everywhere, teetering slightly on their slender legs and baaing softly.

Father enjoyed the role of noble rescuer just about a week, and thereafter the lambs had to be kept out of his way. "Get those creatures out," he bellowed. "I can't stand that infernal racket! All over the place too. I'll dispose of them."

I kept out of sight, too, as much as possible. And, skirting the edge of Father's temper, we got along for a little while. When the storm was very bad, Mamma persuaded me to give one little lamb away to the Mexican boy, who had no pets at all.

But finally, in the end, I got up one morning and there was no sound to greet me. Father was gone, and so was my lamb. He had gone to some mythical heaven, I was to understand, where lambs ran around free and so on.

Nevertheless, I knew Father had something to do with it, and I did not forget it.

If Mamma did not like the little Mexican town, she never complained. There were no stores, so all our clothes and shoes came from Grandma in boxes. There were no social gatherings, there may have been a telephone, but if so, there was nobody to call.

There was a minister and his wife and some kind of little shanty church. So perhaps this was the time that Father was roped into the Methodist fold, and from then on, he and Methodism were involved rather edgily. But his heart was not a fertile valley for religion any more since God had let him down.

Life was relatively even, except for Nellie eating the whole laundry off the line one day. And the weather being dry and hot, and dust sifting over everything.

Then came the starless night when Mamma went to bed early with a sick headache, and I was tucked away in my high-sided bed dreaming of my lost lamb. Father finished his studying and went to bed too, and the only sound was the soft stamping of Raylampego in the shed.

I woke up hearing a strange sound of shouting outside the low window. There was a bright glow over everything, and the noise of the door bolt drawn back.

Then a loud wild cry almost burst my eardrums.

"Fire! Fire!"

Father was plunging around in the room, and Mamma, in her nightgown with her dark hair falling over her face, came swiftly into the flickering light carrying a comforter. She whipped me up into it, fled with me to the door.

I saw the staring dark faces of Mexicans, the night sky, the scrawny arms of Nellie's tree in the yard, and a brilliant torch of fire where the shed had been.

Mamma thrust me into a pair of outstretched arms and vanished into the house. Swiftly I was borne away, buried in that comforter, and the Mexican woman who took me home, laid me on a kind of pallet in a smoky dim hovel where a whole crowd of babbling Mexican women and children spent the rest of the night looking at my blonde hair, darting out to see the progress of the fire, darting back to chatter.

Mama was trying to save a few things. Father was staggering around lifting and tugging at furniture. The Mexicans got in the way and part of the things piled in the yard vanished when they did.

But Father was trying to save the books lent by the French Government and he had armloads so big he couldn't get through the low narrow door with them.

The Socora Fire Department came along. It was a hose wound on a homemade wheel and pulled by two or three Mexicans. There wasn't any water to hook it up to anyway, and in twenty minutes the house had burned to the ground.

Just at the last, Father started in again. Mamma clung to him and he shook her off.

"Don't go back! Don't try it!" she was crying.

"I've got to! I've got to get it!" Father shook her off with such violence that she fell.

Part of the front had fallen and the flames ate up the doorway as Father's figure disappeared in the swirl of smoke. Back into the inferno, he went. Inside, the parlor must have been a mass of flame and smoke.

But Father got out again, carrying a large square object that already had singed edges.

"Majel's portrait!" cried Mamma, running to him.

Father staggered a little, stopped, and looked down, and then laid it at her feet. He ran one blackened hand over his face.

It was the Carom board!

The minister and two other men managed to hold him from another foray into the blazing wreckage, and as he stood struggling to throw them back, the tears blinding his face, there was a sudden billowing of smoke, and the roof fell in.

The Paris Collection, the bulk of the French Government's volumes, the wedding silver, the Hitchcock chairs, and the painting of Majel vanished into a mass of red hot embers.

The grey hand of dawn was lifted above the flaming rubble.

All we had left was our night clothes and the comforter I was wrapped in.

And a fine varnished Carom board!

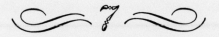

Foreign Invasion

FATHER LOVED MOVING TO MEXICO. MAMMA THOUGHT IT was a little in the nature of gambling to leave the United States and the security of teaching for a job as manager of a mysterious silver mine in the Mexican mountains. But Father could hardly wait to get started.

He sang at the top of his high tenor as he trimmed his moustaches, and he got out all his mining clothes as if he were unpacking the crown jewels again. When he was accoutered, he looked like Custer's last raid, but more beautiful.

The boots laced high, the pants were dun colored, there was a heavy cartridge belt filled with ammunition, a holster holding a blue black revolver, a short ugly hunting knife in an embossed sheath. He made Mamma sew all kinds of extra buttoned pockets in the shirt, for his papers and money. His coat was a kind of hunting jacket with big extra pockets for casual specimens.

He carried a huge canvas bag re-enforced with leather straps that padlocked. An enormous old square camera, boxes and boxes of plates for it, a folding tripod and a black cloth to put over his head while taking pictures went in this, along with his long underwear, socks and some clean soft shirts and handkerchiefs. Then there was the long evil-bladed razor, honed to a paper edge, the honing strap, a bar of shaving soap. There was the geological hammer, which he never moved a step without, for who knew when a rare specimen might leap at you?

Then he had the medicine case. It was as large as a small suitcase, made of thick black leather and opening out flat to display a hundred or more small vials nested in leather pockets. Every drug known to pharmacy was in it, and Father, of course, knew he could manage any emergency with the aid of this noble kit.

Naturally he hadn't had a day of medical training. He was an engineer and geologist. But Father was perfectly confident that he knew all. How he would have loved to be the man who operated for appendicitis in that submarine, following an open book.

The slender white bottles were filled with grey and blue and white powders, as well as aconite pills, rhinitis and all the other lifesavers that had stocked Grandmother's medicine closet.

Mamma persuaded him to pack the cartridge and money belt and the lethal weapons out of sight for the train journey, but when Father boarded the dusty coach, he looked quite spectacular. He topped his costume with a sombrero.

He went without a backward glance, bounding with happiness. A fortune in silver was waiting, a new country, excitement.

Mamma had all the spare cash, which was not much, and the packing to attend to, and the journey with me to the border where we were to wait until Father found a place for us after his first expedition into the Sierra Nevada to look at the mine.

Mamma wasn't quite as excited over the move. She wished she could stay in one place more than long enough to unpack. Besides the country across the border was in an extremely unsettled state. Many Americans were pulling out. Porfirio Diaz was the head of an uneasy land, uprisings and rumors of war sifted back over the Rio Grande.

The only left alive child of this marriage was decidedly delicate, subject to vast and violent stomach upsets, high fevers, and any kind of communicable disease available.

Besides, I had just survived scarlet fever by a pinch, and immediately fallen into whooping cough. I wobbled around like an unfeathered chicken.

But Father had waved his hat and cried happily, "On to Mexico!"

So on we went.

This was not the era of inoculations, but I was scratched for smallpox. Diphtheria was always fatal, a couple of my cousins had already been carried off by it, and one from scarletina. Lung fever was a good killer, and inflammation of the bowels was common. This was probably appendicitis. And Father, of course, had gone into the mountains with all the medicine.

It was summer when we got a room in a boarding house, and Mamma took it for a week. San Antonio was crowded and rooms hard to get. This one was small and uncomfortable, but it was only for a week. Mamma told the landlady she was just waiting for her husband, and she paid in advance for dinner at night.

A good deal of her money had gone in the transportation. So she used to get up early in the hot still morning and go out with a small fish net bag and buy milk and an orange and a roll for me. We ate a sparing lunch at some small restaurant. Mamma never ate much, she wasn't hungry, she said. But I had enough, and now and then a dish of watery ice cream.

We spent the days walking up and down the hot streets or sitting on a park bench. While I took my nap under a white mosquito netting, Mamma wrote home to New England. Sitting at the shaky bare table, dipping her quill in clotted blue ink, she wrote that everything was splendid, it was a very large town, her grey dress with the lace collar was suitable for everything, and Father would be back on Saturday.

After supper, we took another walk while the aching sunlight diminished and the air cooled a little. Possibly because it was a border town, possibly because of the unsettled country so near, or possibly because Mamma had no money, nobody spoke to us at all.

Until Saturday when Mamma flew to the porch for the mail, and there was no mail. Father must have been delayed, so she went to the telegraph office, but there was no telegram either.

"I thought you said your husband would be here at the end of the week," said the landlady, hands on hips, eyes sharp.

"He will be here on Monday," said Mamma cheerfully.

"Then I'll have to ask you for the rent. And board."

Mamma unsewed the little silk packet from the inside of her stiff corset and counted out the money.

The second week we walked to the telegraph office, which was far enough away, every morning and every afternoon.

And Mamma went to the corner to meet the postman. Meals were slimmer.

Mamma was not a narrator like Father, but she did her best to entertain me. There were no books or magazines to read, naturally she could not afford them. At that age, time was what happened as far as I was concerned. I would think we had stayed in that room or walked the streets for years.

The third week, Mamma began to cry in the night, and she looked very pale. She only said that Father was delayed. The landlady was not pleasant about it, but she took the money for the room.

"I notice you haven't got any letters either," she said, hitching up her skirt.

Mama washed my underthings and socks in the bathroom bowl when nobody was around.

We walked. It grew hotter.

I knew something was wrong. I couldn't know how frantic Mamma was, nor how she went over and over the possibilities. Nor the conflict raging under her once-starched shirtwaist. Her pride was high, and she couldn't bear to wire home for help.

And she knew what the Easterners would have to say about Father popping off and leaving us on this wild goose chase after silver. But she was desperate.

If she had no word tomorrow, she would have to wire home. But tomorrow she put it off one more day. And we went walking under trees whose leaves were scorched as if they had been ironed with a too hot iron.

That tomorrow was folded away under a damp pillow,

[141]

and Mamma crept out again for milk and rolls and an orange.

The third week, Mamma was dreadfully quiet. Some band of desperadoes must have set upon Father. He had no tact, and could never, never be diplomatic, no doubt he had insulted some bandit.

And by Saturday the landlady was knocking on the door.

"I'd like to know where this mysterious husband of yours is," she said.

"He's been delayed," said Mamma faintly.

"I don't believe it," said the woman flatly. "There's something peculiar going on here."

"I don't know what you mean," said Mamma.

"I'll have you know this is a respectable house," said the landlady. "I won't stand for any kind of goings on."

Mamma said, "I told you I was staying here until my husband came."

"I don't believe you have a husband," said the landlady. "I don't believe you *ever* had a husband."

Mamma gasped with horror.

"And furthermore, I'll ask you to leave my house at the end of next week. You've had your notice. That's all I have to say on the subject."

The door slammed and I was crying, afraid of something terrible. Mamma stood motionless at the window, her hands clasped. Finally I stopped crying, struck with a sudden thought.

"Father would be awfully mad," I said, "not to be believed in!"

Mamma bathed her face in cool water, and we went out to the telegraph office again.

FOREIGN INVASION

The last of the money was gone by Friday. We would be homeless by Saturday morning, and Mamma waited until afternoon for a last walk to that familiar office. They were tired of her there, too.

"Lady, we'll let you know if there's a wire," they said crossly. "Why don't you just wait to hear?"

Mamma spent some time writing a wire home and she had it folded in her purse. Now the family and all the relatives would know she was at the end of her rope, that Father had vanished, that she had been half-starving in a furnished room for a solid month, and that she was too stiff-necked to have any common sense about anything.

Quite literally, this was the end.

"What are we going to do, Mamma?" I asked, as she brushed my damp curls and tied a ribbon on them.

"Hush, darling, never mind," she said.

The last meal at the boarding house must have been agony. Everybody looked at Mamma with suspicions confirmed. She was a fallen woman, and in that day, a fallen woman was like a leper. They drew their stiff skirts aside as they went by. The servings were small, there was no second offer. I am sure I didn't utter a word, but I always ate everything I could get, so I ate a hearty meal if I could manage it.

We climbed the narrow stairs and Mamma put me to bed early. I could see her, through the veil of mosquito netting, sitting by the window with her head on her hand. The street noises came through the broken screen and the gaslight on the corner gave a yellowish green light to the room.

Suddenly there was a banging at the door, and the land-lady appeared.

"There's a man to see you," she said.

And she was thrust aside roughly as Father burst in. Mamma couldn't even seem to stand up, and Father rushed over and gathered her up in a hearty masculine hug. The landlady's eyes were popping out, and I was clawing at the mosquito netting and screaming with joy.

Mamma was laughing and crying, and the whole dead room was filled with unbearable excitement.

Then Mamma drew herself up and turned to the land-lady and spoke. "I should like you to meet MY HUSBAND," she said.

Father was real, all right. He was brown as a coffee berry and little squinting wrinkles fanned around his eyes. His clothes were dusty, his boots weathered. The canvas bag was stained. He had a new sombrero, with a very wide brim and a real silver headband.

"I've brought you lots of presents," he said happily. "I've had lots of adventures! Wait until I tell you all about them!"

"But what *happened* to you?" cried Mamma, "I thought you were dead! I thought you were killed!"

Father looked at her in astonishment. "Whatever gave you a crazy notion like that?" he asked. "Nothing could possibly happen to me!"

"I didn't hear a single word in all this time!"

"I had to stay over at the mine," he explained. "It's ninety miles in the mountain from the last village by pack trail. So I couldn't very well write." He came over and picked me up. "You're getting big," he said. "Did you have a good time?"

"No," I said.

"They have a bright green parrot in the village," said Father, "and he talks all the time. He belongs to the man who keeps the inn and he has a cage in the patio. The patio is full of flowers. The mountains are wonderful. Indians live there. I bought one of their blankets, woven all of black wool." Father put me down, and I sat on the edge of the bed.

"We rode all day," he told Mamma, "over trails so narrow that if the pony struck a stone, it fell a thousand feet down! Once there was a big rattlesnake coiled in the middle of the trail, ready to strike. My pony jumped over it. It struck a pack burro instead."

"Then what?" I asked.

"The burro died. But I shot the snake," said Father. "The Indians are mostly Tarahumaris. I had a mozo for a day or so who could out-run a deer. They have races, too, and they run all day. The women," he said impressively to Mamma, "run all day and kick a wooden ball ahead of them. I bought one of the balls. When they run a deer they run any length of time. The deer gets ahead, of course, but they run on. They carry parched corn or something to eat as they go, and they just keep going until the deer wears out. I got along fine with them. I cured a sick child."

"What did it have?"

"Well, I am not sure," he admitted. "But I mixed up several powders from the medicine kit and gave it all of them and it got better right away."

Mamma said, "I was so worried, I nearly died."

"I don't see why," said Father.

"What are we going to do?" asked Mamma.

"We're going to live in Chihuahua. I found a place," he said. "It's upstairs over a Mexican family, but we'll get a house later." He wasn't much interested in that. "Gladys will have to go to a Mexican school, that's all there is. Between trips to the mine, I'll be there. I have to carry the pay once a month in silver, and I'll go at a different time every month. The mountains are full of desperadoes." He was moving around unpacking and fishing for clean socks now.

"I had quite an adventure," he said happily, "at a mountain inn. A couple of desperadoes had the next room and there was just a thin partition. They got to fighting and they were slashing around with knives. The innkeeper wanted me to go away and hide because they would kill a gringo in a minute when they were stirred up. I had to sit up all night with my revolver ready to draw. I told that Mexican if they could draw any quicker or throw a knife before I got 'em, I'd just as soon be dead anyway. In the morning I went out and did a little target shooting in the yard just as an illustration. They never bothered me at all."

Mamma said, "And this is the kind of life we are going to have?"

"It's a wonderful country," said Father enthusiastically. "And the mountains are rich with silver. Never saw anything like it. Wonderful country. Only thing wrong with it is all those Mexicans."

"But it's their country," said Mamma feebly.

"Terrible mistake," said Father. "We ought **never** to

have let that country slip away and be run by a bunch of ignorant Mexicans. Diaz is an old robber, the peasants are starving, the Indians are a lost race, and the place is a sink of sin and disease in the cities. A good Republican administration would do wonders. But wait until you see the floating gardens at Xochimilco and Popocatepetl! And the flower market in Mexico City!"

"It isn't too late to go back home," said Mamma, "and be in a civilized land."

"We ought to pack tonight," said Father. "We better get the early train in the morning. We'll never get there if we don't get started." He added, "You'll have a nice friend there, a Mrs. Willis. She lives right near. She'll be company for you. Her husband is in jail and she just waits around."

Mamma gasped.

"He's an American engineer," said Father. "He didn't do anything. He's just as respectable as I am. Some spy or other reported him for drawing a map or something, and he's been incommunicado for a month."

Mamma said, "You'll be the next one! Oh, I know it! Oh, why did this have to come up?"

"Nonsense," said Father. "I told you there's nothing at all to worry about. I wouldn't get stuck in one of those jails. They're murderous places." He said, "I didn't get around to seeing a bull fight but the Governor's bulls are used every Sunday, and they have a regular fiesta. I'll take you to one as soon as we get settled."

Then he looked around the room. "This is a hole," he said, "and that numbskull who runs the house wasn't very anxious to let me in. I suppose we may as well stay here overnight, but she's not going to charge extra."

[147]

He produced a purple silk handkerchief and wiped his face.

"Is the food fit to eat in the dining room? Or shall we go out? That Mexican food is good, but it burns your tonsils out. I'd like a steak and some apple pie."

Then an afterthought struck him. "Did you have enough money?"

Mamma looked at him, and suddenly she laughed. She laughed until the tears ran down her face. So I laughed too.

It was all a great joke.

The house was white, glaring in the hot sun, and the flat where we lived was small. There was an upper balcony in the back where you could look down on the yard of the Mexican family that lived next door. They kept game chickens, a couple of thin mangy dogs, and lots of children. Father decided I would catch something if I went over there, so I could only wonder what they were going to do next.

We had only just settled when they decided to clean house. Maybe one of the older daughters was getting married. There was a great racketing about all day long, things were shaken out in the yard, blankets whacked at with brooms. I was entertained all day, watching.

The next morning I woke up feeling feverish and upset. I was also itching all over. Mamma came running in when I called her and gave one look at me.

Then she shouted for Father. "She's coming down with something again!" she wailed despairingly.

Father, his long razor in his hand, poked his head in

the door, and said, "What's the matter?" He said, "She just needs some exercise and fresh air."

Now this was curious about him. On the one hand he was a constant doser and taker of medicines, on the other hand he never would admit that anyone was really sick. Sickness frightened him, and did not enter into his plan for the world. It made him nervous when I had anything, and he refused to believe even in my catching scarlet fever. He always felt I should get up and take some exercise and throw it off.

He also stayed out of the room. If anyone were really ill, Father was a terrible problem. He was angry, he banged around. He felt someone was persecuting him personally by the inconvenience and the worry.

Not being in any sense of the word a brooder, he never felt that he was inconsistent.

"She's broken out all over!" cried Mamma.

"It's the heat," he said, still in the doorway. "I'll give her some aconite and rhinitis, and she can have a Seidlitz powder later. She better get right up and get some fresh air and exercise and have a good breakfast."

Mamma was bending over me, her hand on my flushed face. The spots itched and burned like small separate fires.

"I don't feel good," I said.

Mamma gave another cry. "You come here and look!" she demanded. "There's blood on the sheet! Oh, I knew we shouldn't have come to this awful place!"

Father had to step in and make a gingerly approach to the bed. He gave me one look.

"Bedbugs," he said.

Mamma screamed. I bolted from bed.

"Bedbugs," he said again.

We were united in horror.

Nothing probably compares with the feeling a New Englander has about any form of insect. It is a sin to have so much as a small spider in the attic. And bedbugs indicate a degree of degradation awful to contemplate. Quite aside from their being dreadful little creatures in themselves, and that they bite, neither Mamma nor Father would have believed anyone could get into Heaven who had ever been introduced to the small bedbug.

I, of course, felt like a pariah. No nice person would ever speak to me again. I was an outcast from life. All the while Mamma was scrubbing me with yellow soap and almost boiling water, I was facing the fact that my life as a Christian and decent citizen was ended.

Father, meanwhile, was organized into fearful activity. Here was an enemy in his own house. He threw things out of the window into the yard. Furniture was piled in one room. Curtains came down. Pictures, just hung a few days ago, were unhung and stacked. Rugs flew through the air.

The stench of my mattress burning added to the general confusion. Dried off, and dressed in clean clothes, I was perched in a straight chair in the front room. I didn't need to be told to stay there, I was afraid to set foot anywhere.

Mamma, with kerosene, lye, hot water, soap, disinfectant, and scrub brushes, attacked the bedsprings and the bed itself. Father bolted out to the pharmacy and came back with a bag of enormous sulphur candles.

"I'll fix them," he said, savagely.

More activity ensued. The bedrooms were sealed up.

Paper strips were pasted around the windows and the sulphur candles set in and lighted. The doors were closed and sealed up outside with more paper.

Whatever the effect was on the bedbugs, it was nearly fatal to the family. For sulphur candles are powerful, and they send their suffocating odor even into the walls. I could smell it in my sleep after the rooms were habitable again and I had been put to bed in the aromatic added smell of kerosene which seeped up to me from below.

Mamma's theory was that Father had "brought them in" from the mountains. Father, insulted, vowed they were left behind by the previous tenants. There was quite a battle over this, but finally they quieted down and went to bed too.

"At least that's over," said Father.

In the middle of the night, I woke up and called to Mamma.

"Mamma, something's biting me again!"

"Nonsense, it's your imagination," said Mamma. "Go to sleep."

"But I felt . . ."

"Be quiet!" Father thundered. "You're only imagining things."

I fell into an uneasy sleep, with considerable twitching and tossing. Father couldn't be wrong, so there was nothing else to do.

But in the morning, I was covered with red spots again. Father's reaction almost shattered the building. I know exactly how the natives on an atoll feel when the hurricane sweeps them into the sea. They feel like we felt with Father blowing full gale over the bedbugs.

ESPECIALLY FATHER

While Mamma persuaded him not to set a stick of dynamite under the house, I slipped out to the balcony to be out of sight. I leaned on the railing and looked down.

It was peaceful below in the morning sun. The Mexicans had finished their housecleaning. A few game roosters scratched in the dust. And there was a small line of moving color threading its way up to the wall and rising against the chalk white rough surface. I watched it with interest, and then with sudden shock.

Then I screamed for Father, and he came billowing out in his night shirt, and looked where my shaky finger pointed.

A solid battalion of bedbugs was steadily advancing up that wall, an army on the move. The ranks were unbroken, the line was wide. It may be science does not concede any concerted troop movement on the part of bedbugs. I have never done any research myself in the habits of bedbugs. But science or no science, those bedbugs were moving from the Mexican house to our house, where presumably there would be no housecleaning to disturb them. And all the while Mamma and Father had been struggling with the advance horde, this new army had been creeping up over the railing and getting inside on the balcony.

The rest of that day is nothing to write about. The Mexicans next door must have decided the gringos were mad. International relations were at the lowest ebb in history after Father went over there and, in the peculiar Spanish he had picked up, told them what was wrong with them, with their house, with their country. He had the idea then, too, that if he shouted loud enough, they would understand.

We moved.

This time we lived downstairs and in spite of the upper

tenants being addicted to tequila in the middle of the night, we stayed for awhile, because we had to.

Mamma had a severe headache one day shortly after unpacking. It was the day of sick headaches. Nobody ever bothered to find out what made these headaches. Migraine, some of them. Nerves, some must have been, sinus was unknown, allergy had not reared its hydra head. Mamma simply had sick headaches now and then. She went to bed with a damp cloth over her eyes and the smelling salts at hand in the dark clear green bottle stoppered with silver.

But this headache got so bad that she couldn't seem to stand it, although Mamma and pain were on a good easy footing always.

Father was away all day, getting ready for a trip to the mine, and Mamma had me bring her cool water every little while. She roused herself to tell me to get something to eat from the cupboard, and then she seemed to be asleep, but she made strange low sounds as she slept. The beds were covered with big tents of heavy netting, and I could see her through the diffused light, her face very red and her hair falling over the pillow.

We didn't know anybody except the woman in black, Mrs. Willis, who had come and cried steadily a couple of afternoons. Her husband was still in jail and she still could not get the charges. They always told her mañana. I wished she would come in now, even though her crying made me nervous.

The afternoon thinned away to a slice of light. Mamma woke up and it was time to get supper, but she only turned her head away from the window and said something in a language I couldn't understand. The words were heavy and almost indistinct.

Finally I heard the quick impatient steps I was aching for, and ran to meet Father. The heels of his boots sounded loud. He had his papers under his arm, his sombrero tilted at a sharp angle, his coat open. Hard riding and outdoor camping in the mountains agreed with him. He was lean and lithe, his face was the color of an old bronze coin, and his eyes looked even bluer against the color of his skin. Looking long distances in the bright light had given him little extra wrinkles from squinting, but otherwise he looked as young as a boy.

But his mouth was losing its sensitive curve. Father got mad so often, and he had a way of pulling down the upper lip when he was upset. Now his mouth was just beginning to get a straight thinner look from that upper lip being pinched down.

He wore his cartridge belt empty, but tightened around his slim waist.

He looked, as a matter of fact, not unlike the bandits he was always watching for along the trails.

I flew to him. Mamma was in bed, I said, with one of her headaches. His lip drew down, he was hungry and wanted a good meal. He strode in.

Mamma sat up and spoke.

Even Father knew something more than a headache was wrong, for her words made no sense. He got out the black leather medicine kit and mixed up two or three powders and sent me for a glass of water, and made her drink the mixture.

"Mamma's sick!" I began to cry.

"Certainly not!" he said. "She's just got a little fever. Touch of the sun." He stared at me. "She can't be sick!"

I don't remember how we ate. Father's cooking was limited to eggs and bacon. By the time Grandmother had taught her four girls to cook, all she asked of the boys was to keep out from underfoot. He could make good coffee, black and strong.

Mamma couldn't eat or drink the coffee. Now Father always denied illness to be true, with a queer belief that if he insisted there was nothing to worry about, there wouldn't be. He kept telling me Mamma just had a little fever, and all the time he was tramping around, sopping wet washcloths on her burning head, opening the windows, then shutting them again. Trying to dose her with his various kinds of pills.

But Mamma lay in a dull stupor now, and nothing he did made her any better.

In the morning, Father clapped on the sombrero and went for the doctor. This was one of the few times he admitted a need of one.

"She's eaten something that poisoned her," he said. "If she can get up and get out, she'll be all right."

I wasn't any help. Mamma had never stayed in bed in the daytime in my whole life except for a few hours with a headache. She never took any pills or powders or had any symptoms of anything. If she had a pain anywhere, she ignored it. And Father and I both founded our world on the sure Gibraltar of her strength. All of Chihuahua might have collapsed in an earthquake and we would have been all right. But with Mamma in bed, the universe was disintegrated into primal chaos.

The doctor came after a long while. He was an American, and overworked year in and year out. I suppose, under Diaz, most of the government funds went to sustain the army that kept him where he was, and with the whole country in a ferment and talk of a revolution over every coffee cup, it is no wonder medical services were scant.

Father was tramping around in a frenzy. The aconite hadn't made a dent in the fever, and Mamma had not gotten up and dressed and gone out for that fresh air and exercise. She was right under the tent of mosquito netting.

The doctor wearily put down his black bag and went over to make an examination and a diagnosis. I was sent out of the room. Eternity passed. When I couldn't stand it any longer, I poked my face back in.

Father and the doctor were both standing up, and the doctor was putting away his stethoscope.

"There isn't much doubt about it," he said. "Your wife has typhoid fever!"

"She can't have!"

"She has," said the doctor. "There's every indication. It's typhoid fever."

Father was almost as delirious as Mamma. But not even his storming changed the situation. And the doctor had no magic pill to bring Mamma back to health. There were no hospital facilities, there were no nurses, but he would try to get some woman to come in and help out.

"A trained nurse would be worth a million dollars," he said, in parting. "I'll do what I can. I'll come in again in the morning."

Now Father's world of adventure changed into a God-forsaken country. He had done nothing at all to deserve this

[156]

blow, he was an upright man, he always did his duty. The injustice of it bit into his soul.

Mamma had so carefully boiled my drinking water and his, but she hated the flat taste of boiled water herself, and sometimes she had indulged in a nice fresh glass of unboiled water. She never dreamed for a moment that she could get sick.

For six infinite weeks, she was desperately ill, and I think only the determination to survive brought her out of it in the end. But Mamma wouldn't give in. She wasn't going to have another woman raising her child or taking care of her husband.

But it was a long time before Father extolled the wonders of Mexico again.

Mamma being up and about again, life went back to normal. That is, we moved. This time we had a whole house, with a nice patio that you could play in if you watched for scorpions and vinagrones. I remember the front door very well, for there was a place at one side where we hid the key when we went away.

One day I came home with Father and a friend, and the friend made some casual remark about hoping Father had his key, and I piped up innocently, "Oh, we hide the key right at the side. See over there!"

After the friend had gone, Father thrashed me until I was black and blue. It was a beating I can feel even now. His face was black, too, with rage. When I could, I sobbed, "But what have I done, Father?"

"I'll teach you to keep your mouth shut about things," he said.

Mamma came home about then, and when she had separated us and bathed my face, and my tears were all shed, I managed to find out that I had sinned by divulging the hiding place of the key. Mamma tried to explain how wicked it was. There were many things you never told, I was to understand.

It was very hazy in my mind. If the house were robbed, would the friend be the one because he knew about the key? I couldn't figure it out.

But after supper, Father forgave me, and we both cried, and he said the words he said so often, "Just be a good girl. Try to be a good girl."

"I do try," I said, my arms around his neck, our tears mingling.

But Mamma did not speak to him at all that night. Her ideas of justice didn't quite match his.

Mamma usually said nothing when she was upset. Father, on the other hand, said everything he could think of. He flared up like Fourth of July, and when it was over, he expected the whole thing to be forgotten. It was just unfortunate that Mamma was so different. Once she said something, it was said for all time. If Mamma said she would never forgive anyone for anything, she never did. So she was chary of her words.

Father never understood why he couldn't blow off with abandon and then have us all forget the trouble as fast as he did.

"What in the world is the matter with you *now?*" he would ask innocently, after he had stormed and banged around and his personal sky was summer-serene.

Mamma wouldn't say anything.

But one time, she said a good deal. Father took me off

to town when he was shopping around for some jewels. He had a great passion for uncut stones, or unset jewels. His eye was excellent and he was a fine hand at beating the sellers down. He bought a perfect ruby which was his favorite. But usually he contented himself with semi-precious stones which he could more or less afford. He bought zircons, turquoise, garnets, tourmaline, chalcedony, opals. He bought rose quartz, onyx, jade, anything with beauty of color.

Sometimes he had them set for Mamma for presents, and sometimes he just kept them, to take out and look at. If anyone had told him he was a born collector, he would have been furious. He simply had a chance to get really good things now and then, and got them.

This day he took me along as a special favor, probably to make up for the spanking the day before. We went to a Mexican jeweler's, and I watched while the salesman rolled out a box full of glowing or cloudy green and red and blue and brown stones.

Father told me the history of every one, where it came from, how it was cut. I even held a flawed turquoise in my hand, and wished passionately that I might have it. There was a piece of topaz too, like sunlight on brown water. Moved by the look on my face, Father said, "You may have one. Which would you like?"

Oh, the awful agony of decision! The stone like blue-green water or the stone with the sun in the deep part of it? I hung over the case, my pigtails fairly shaking.

"Make up your mind," said Father, impatiently.

I held one. I held the other. I wavered. I chose the blue, then I chose the brown. I let the sunlight fall on each one.

"All right," said Father. "If you can't make up your mind, you can't have either one." And he picked them up and gave them back to the salesman, and went on with his own selection which was like lightning.

Since that day, I have made up my mind in a hurry. People who wonder how I could buy a fur coat in ten minutes, or decide on a house in five, have no way of seeing the thin little girl in the Mexican jeweler's with no blue stone and no brown to cherish.

Father wanted that day to look in at another place, and he didn't want to measure his rapid gait by mine, so he said, "You wait right here, I'll be back in a minute."

He vanished, and the salesman went about his business. I stood just where Father left me, craning my neck to look in the case, and telling myself stories about the rings and bracelets, the carved silver pins and combs.

I stood on one foot and then on the other. After a time, the man came back and asked me if I was still there, which I thought was a silly question. I answered him in my politest Spanish. Going to a Mexican school, I spoke Spanish better than English.

The sun moved across the floor very slowly. I walked around the counter a little. People came in and bought things and went away. The salesman went out to lunch and another one took over. Everything stilled for the siesta period. I wished I could have something to eat or find a place to sit down.

Late in the afternoon, the salesman began to ask me questions.

"Father told me to wait right here," I said.

The manager came in and they talked it over. The day

was passing and they didn't know what to do with this child. I was pretty tired of standing around, and my head ached because I was hungry.

Father had a fine time. He ran down a number of very cheap and very good stones. He got some bargains. He had something to eat somewhere when he was hungry, and went on. He had some other business to attend to, and finally at the end of the day when things were closing up anyway, he went home.

Mamma was getting supper and when he came in, she looked up.

"I've got some fine things," he said happily.

Mamma dropped whatever she had in her hand. "Where's Gladys?"

Father said, "Good gracious, I forgot all about her!"

"What?" cried Mamma. "What? What did you do with her?"

"I left her somewhere," said Father. "Now let me see—" Then he started for the door. "Now don't worry," he said, "I'll be right back with her."

Mamma spoke. "You bring her back," she said, "or don't come back yourself!"

About this time, the Mexicans had decided Father had deserted me. They were planning on where to take me, when Father dashed in. "Oh, here you are," he said, grabbing my hand. "Come on. Your mother's worried."

He felt Mamma was very unfair to be so angry at him. I had only slipped his mind. I was perfectly safe. He'd had a lot on his mind. Mamma said I might have been kidnapped and they'd never see me again. Mamma said if I hadn't been good and stayed there, I might have been

[161]

killed. She said quite a lot of things, and Father got mad, and I kept out of the way. I didn't see what the excitement was all about.

I only wished I had been able to decide quicker between the turquoise and the topaz.

When I went to bed, Father held me in his arms and kissed me and forgave me for everything and presented me with a garnet or a zircon or something. I don't even remember what the present was.

But Mamma had reason to be disturbed, for things were getting worse in the country. Some Americans had already pulled up stakes and gone home. Everyone was very careful as to what they said about Diaz or Villa or the government. The mining people were worried.

The miners would work a day or so and then stop and celebrate. Father made a hurried trip, and it was more dangerous than it had ever been. He rode without stopping in any mountain inn. He pushed the horse. And at the mine, he fired the Mexican manager.

The silver was there and the men idling around. But the manager was an important figure, and his brother was a priest, and the men were ugly when Father told the man to get out and stay out.

The day Father got back, the manager and the priest came to see him at home. I wondered a little why Mamma stayed right in the front room all the time, her sewing in her lap. I stayed too, looking at the dark angry strangers and at Father's set grim mouth. They all argued and the Mexicans waved their arms. The air crackled.

But Father put them out, with far more courage than

sense. In the doorway, one of them turned and shook his closed fist. Father slammed the door and bolted it.

Mamma tried to persuade him to take the manager back, just to keep peace, but Father would have none of it. "He's lazy," he said. And that settled it.

We had a subdued supper. "We ought to go back to the States," said Mamma, "the revolution is coming any day. Everyone is going. It isn't safe."

"I won't be driven out," said Father, setting his lips together. "No bunch of Mexicans is going to scare me away."

It must have been around nine o'clock when Mamma suddenly looked up at the window and gasped. The night was black, and the heavy window bars made dark lines against it. The shades were down, of course, but there was a small space at the bottom between the shade and the sill.

Into this space, from the outer darkness, a long dark hand was creeping, pushing a thick square of black cloth. The cloth filled the space, the hand was now hidden in the folds.

Father made a signal for us to keep quiet and we hardly breathed. There was no sound from outside either, not a footfall, not a movement. The light went out. Father had put it out so quietly I had not heard him move.

The death warning was still visible, a darker mass in the darkness. Father was quick enough to figure that if he opened the door, even he would not have time to pull his trigger. If he had, he would be hung for murder without benefit of trial.

Maybe they were hoping he would fire at that black cloth. And if Mamma and I had been out of the room, he might have ended his journey then and there, with a companion.

But Father was motionless, Mamma's breathing was no more than a sigh, and I held my breath until my eyes popped and then drew in just a smidgen of air.

And after an endless time, the hand very slowly moved back, withdrawing the cloth. There was no sound of footsteps, but after a half hour more of waiting in the silent room, Father slid to the window and lifted the edge of the shade.

"They've gone," he said, in a perfectly calm voice.

"They'll kill you!" said Mamma. "We've got to get away!"

"I won't run away from anybody," said Father, pulling his lip down. "That's what they want!"

Mamma couldn't make any impression on him. He went out the next day with his revolver clean and loaded, and Mamma never expected to see him again.

His luck held, as it always did, and before there was a mysterious disappearance of a mining engineer, the general situation politically grew so acute, that the mine was closed down, and Father could, with dignity withdraw himself and his family from the foreign country.

Mamma in some way exerted enough influence on him to get him to accept a teaching position in the middlewest, and give up mining engineering, at least for awhile. I had to go to school in one spot for a little time, she said, or I'd grow up into an uneducated heathen.

How reluctantly Father packed up his boots and spurs,

his hand-woven rope lariat, the cartridge belt and the ugly blue revolver. Boxes and boxes of minerals and ore were packed and shipped. The Indian blankets and serapes were nourished with mothballs for their storage.

The beautiful sombrero, the bright silk handkerchiefs, the scarves, all were packed, together with the presents Mamma was taking back to relatives.

Our clothes went in an enormous trunk with two trays and brass bound corners and locks. It was big enough for a playhouse, and it was full.

Father went out to do a last errand or two, and Mamma had the top tray filled when he came back. He had a rolled parcel in one hand and he was grinning happily. He unwrapped it and held up a very large, very brightly colored picture. It was the virgin, in a lurid blue robe, holding a bright pink baby. Whoever originated it had let himself go on color, and had considerable difficulty making the faces look faintly human.

But it was bright.

"Whatever has gotten into you?" said Mamma.

Father produced a handful of thumb tacks from his vest pocket and going over to the trunk, tacked the pictures on the inside of the lid, so whenever the trunk was open, the startling vision of Madonna and child looked out.

"There," said Father, with satisfaction, "I guess that'll get us through the customs all right."

And it did.

Mamma was more than thankful to return to the United States. At least the family would be safe and there was no prospect of a revolution, whether the Democrats or the Republicans won the next election.

[165]

But Father looked back across the wide oily-colored waters of the Rio Grande with longing.

It all seemed pretty tame to Father, to live in a flat midwestern town and teach geology, instead of bucketing about in a wild and dangerous mountain. And nobody could discover a hidden lode on a campus. Fortunes lay buried in the lost mountains, but the salary of an assistant Professor was below sea level.

Moving again, that was what I thought. An American school where all the children spoke English and would laugh at me.

Father summed up his return to the land of his birth as we climbed on the hot dusty train and settled ourselves on sandpapery seats.

"We'll go back there, as soon as things settle down." He said, "It's a wonderful country! If only it didn't belong to all those foreigners!"

The Elms on the Campus

A COLLEGE CAMPUS IS OFTEN THOUGHT OF AS A PEACEFUL ivory tower sort of place, far from the maddening rush of real life. The elms on the campus murmur softly in the college songs, and under the arching shadows of serene maples the young and innocent walk to classes with books under their arms and dreams in their heads.

To Father, however, a college was simply a place where students could study geology. The basic subject. Geology led to mineralogy, paleontology. It was all right to take a few extra subjects such as Latin and Greek and physics and chemistry, but these were more or less padding. The main thing was to understand *geology*.

The first thing he did was to institute field trips which took hours and hours of time. The geology classes were snapped up and whipped about the countryside at a terrific pace. They climbed cliffs, sped through barbed wire fences, crossed streams on rotting planks, sank in mud to their knees. Once off with Father to study a few formations, they were lucky to get back alive.

Even the football players were tired when Father got through. Disheveled and scratched, the students would limp along with Father leaping ahead like a lively Excelsior.

They lugged specimens too. Not just small chips, but

sacks of heavy granites and glacier-scratched stones, hunks of ore, and incidentally Indian stone tomahawk heads and spear points.

The survivors of the field trips were fascinated, and the weaker ones transferred to something quieter like biology. "I just couldn't stand those field trips," one girl said once. "They were killing me."

Father felt that he was the most fair-minded of all men. It was purely coincidence that the students he liked best got the highest marks. He couldn't help it if his teaching was on a highly personal basis, for so was all the rest of his life. He expected a great deal of work, and when a student he really liked wrote a poor paper, Father was insulted.

His method of teaching was purely personal too, and I often wish I could see a student's notebook from those early days. If anyone could outline Father, I would be amazed. He simply talked about what interested him.

The students overran the house. A casual visitor might have thought our house was an extension of the dormitory. They brought presents too. We usually had a couple of ducks and chickens tethered in the cellar during the school session. They brought fish from White River, Indian relics from Sheboygan, melons from Winneconnie, cheese from Monroe.

Father's way of accepting a gift was anything but gracious. He would grin, blush awkwardly, and say, "What's this? Well, well." I never heard him say thank you to any of them, but they didn't care.

He expected all of his students to behave the way he thought was right. Unfortunate the girl who put on enough

THE ELMS ON THE CAMPUS

lipstick to be noticeable, Father's cold stare was uncomfortable. And the day he caught one of his own boys kissing one of his own girls in the dim corridor outside the laboratory was a dreadful one.

"Right outside my own laboratory," he fumed.

"I expect they are just getting engaged," said Mamma tactfully. "I wouldn't notice it."

"No business at all," snapped Father. "Takes their minds off their work. Ought to be suspended."

"You can't keep youngsters from falling in love," said Mamma, "especially when the lilacs are in bloom."

Father gave a lecture on behavior the next day. People came to college for an education, he said, and not for lightminded carryings on.

It was fortunate that the students in the midwest of that day were usually simple, unsophisticated boys and girls. They did not drive their own cars, it was not customary to carry private flasks, and gambling went only as far as a few quarters on fan-tan. Roadhouses had not sprouted on every corner, and dancing went on in the gymnasium with chaperons. Girls wore stockings, and no one had heard of loafers. Father would never have let a modern college girl in his class, with a pair of rolled jeans and a man's shirt and bobbysocks and overrun loafers. He would have thought, and said, she was crazy.

But times were changing and one day I bobbed my hair. Coming home from the beauty parlor (girls did not patronize the barber), I met Father loping along the campus. He looked at me and walked on past with no word. I was considerably frightened, and it wasn't until after supper that

[169]

I saw him look at me sharply and heard him say, "What's the matter with you? What have you done to your hair?" He had not recognized me at all.

Boys who came to see me learned to smoke a furtive cigarette by kneeling down on the hearth and blowing the smoke up the chimney. There was no smoking on campus.

Father's estimate of a grown man was easy to predict.

"He can't amount to much," he would say. "He smokes like a chimney."

Teaching full time, of course, did not make a dent in Father's energy. He took over the college museum too. The museum was on the top floor of the science building, and in those dim and dusty rooms was piled everything anyone had ever donated to the college. Everything was dumped together, Hindu robes, African masks, totem poles, steel engravings of Madison, Wisconsin, in 1850, stuffed eagles, a glassy-eyed tuna fish on a board, hundreds of Indian arrowheads, broken bits of pottery from Butte De Mort, Egyptian scarabs, hunks of metal, old hair-wreaths, Civil War letters and diaries. Moths and rats and spiders throve happily.

Things people did not know what to do with always came "as a gift to the college museum."

It took a brave soul to attack this welter of junk. But Father drafted a couple of his pet boys and waded in. It was a disgrace, he said furiously, for a college to have a museum in that condition. Look at the Smithsonian Institute, he said, look at the museum in Milwaukee, look at the Natural History Museum—

"Well, you can hardly compete with them," said Mamma.

"I don't see why not," he said.

Cleaning up and organizing the exhibits might have seemed an innocuous pursuit, but not when Father was doing it. He threw out what was no good, no matter who the donor might be. He discarded one whole set of bones because it was nothing but a cow, he said, and whoever thought they were Indian bones was crazy. He threw the bones in the dump.

Part of the arrows were rank fakes, too, he said, and the man who had sold them to the college ought to be sued. This man was not pleased. Father pointed out that the stone was not the type the Indians used and that a metal instrument had obviously sharpened the points.

Father, in short, looked every gift horse in the mouth.

Next he attacked the board for more money to really build up the museum. He was alone in the battle. The other professors wanted money for their own pursuits. Father got some money.

Toward the end of the collossal task, he worked many nights as well as days. With Higgins' black indelible ink and a fine steel pen, he spent hours printing labels in his best hand, which looked like engraving. All of the smaller exhibits went under the microscope.

Finally one night he decided to air the black bear. This was a large erect bear with a big open red mouth and lifted forepaws. It had been shot in the woods in an earlier day and was a gift from a special family.

The bear had moths. Father was laboriously mounting the last of the arrow heads, when he happened to look up and see a few moths fluttering under the black bear's chin.

How Father and the bear got down the stairs is a mystery

[171]

to this day, but down they got, and Father left the bear by the steps of the science building to air while he went home for supper. Then he forgot him, because he got involved in cementing the garage floor.

The black bear spent the night standing by the steps, and it was a good thing for him, but a couple of girls coming home late from the library looked up to see him looming above them in the shadowy night and went into screaming fits.

They roused the night watchman, who was frightened too, and the whole campus was in a terrible state. Father was asked to take his bear back upstairs the next day.

Father said it was extremely silly, a bear does not attack unless you irritate him. Besides this was a dead bear.

But a campus legend had started. Father and his bear went down in history with the cow that Dr. Reeve and his friends had put in the belfry and that nobody could get down. The cow moaned for two days before the fire department managed to snag her back. Father's bear was a lesser but pleasant tale.

About this time, came Father's battle with the trustees. He failed the son of a very wealthy trustee, and the failure was just the one that meant the boy could not stay in college.

The trustee felt, quite reasonably, that his son should stay in college. He was giving a large sum to the new library but not if his own child could not draw a book therefrom.

The president called Father in for a conference. He tactfully suggested Father might give extra help to the boy, give him a new examination.

"He failed," said Father.

"But in this special case . . ."

"He failed," said Father. "He made sixty-five, and seventy is passing."

Of course Father didn't like the boy anyway. "Doesn't amount to a hill of beans," he told Mamma. "I saw him lighting a cigarette on the street." He added, "Cuts classes too."

This was the end of it. That anyone should not wish to be in class listening to Father was enough.

"He almost passed," urged Mamma. "Couldn't you just raise him to seventy?" Mamma didn't see why anyone should fail anyway.

"Right is right," said Father sternly. "And you can't compromise."

The matter was brought up in faculty meeting. Any faculty meeting is a pitched battle, but this one was particularly rugged and afterward nobody knew who was still speaking to whom.

Father did not change the grade. Some other professor had to add a point or so, and a special rule was fixed up so the boy could stay on, at least until the library fund was secure.

It made Father mad every time he thought of it.

"No use marking at all," he said. "Just as well give everybody an A and have done with it. I ought to resign."

About once a week something disturbed him enough so he decided to resign. Mamma never paid much attention. For one thing, she was pretty busy. We had so many students for meals, and then there was the Town and Gown Club and the Clio Club and the church suppers, and faculty dinners. And the girls began to drop in and talk over their troubles with her, for Mamma was the kind of woman nobody could resist confiding in.

Besides all the activity of a professor's wife, Mamma kept house, did our washing with the help of a day woman once a week, made her own hats and some of my clothes. And picked up after Father.

The house was full of my gang too, there was never a quiet moment.

"Just put it all out of your mind," she said to Father finally. "It's all over. It doesn't do any harm for that one boy to stay. He's a nice kind boy."

"I ought to resign," Father muttered. But next week he forgot about it.

This battle was a quick one. But there was another, in later years, which was long drawn out. I was the unhappy instigator.

Father never got on very well with the librarian. She was a perfectly nice spinster, whom I shall call Miss March, but she did not really like to have books taken out of the library. She liked them on the shelves, in their proper places. Father was always taking them out and getting his students to take them out. And he wanted more books of reference for his own subject than the whole library appropriation for the faculty.

So they were not too warm friends to begin with. Also, Father was not very quiet in the hushed environs of the library. He couldn't even walk quietly. And when he came into a room, it was as if a sudden electric current had been turned on. He would rush in, overcoat flung open, books in his arms, bang them on the desk, ask for what he wanted in a strong voice, and ask for it in a hurry. He never bothered to sign for anything either. Well, maybe once in awhile. If he did, he would lose the slip, or bring the books back and not cross them off.

While he was going over these matters with Miss March, all the students would stop reading, and jiggle around and make a whispering noise.

But this might have gone on without a crisis except for me. The rules of the library were inflexible, Miss March thought. One of them was with regard to the length of time a graduate student could keep a book out. A teacher could keep books out as long as needed, but not a graduate student.

A graduate student could keep them out a little longer than an undergraduate, that was all. After that, a fine was charged for overtime.

The day came when I was working on my thesis on Shelley and I took out a book of Shelley's letters. I kept it out several weeks. I was teaching a class of Freshman Composition and all the themes came in so I was held up on the thesis.

Came the day I got a card from Miss March, billing me seventy-five cents for overtime on Shelley. We were having supper when I went over the mail, I believe, and I tossed the card to Father.

"I've got a seventy-five cent fine," I said. "I thought I could keep books out as long as I needed them."

Father rose up in his seat and laid down his knife and took the card. The slow red was coming up in his face. "What's this? What's this?" he said. "She can't fine you! You're a teacher!" He pocketed the card. "I'll speak to her," he said darkly.

"Gladys better take care of it," said Mamma. "She can just explain."

"Explain!" said Father, "Miss March can explain!"

"Oh, dear me," said Mamma, "don't argue with her, dear. Just go on and pay it. It's only seventy-five cents!"

"Only seventy-five cents!" said Father.

I was worried. Nobody ever was more law-abiding than I, or more timid. Rarely did Father's blood begin to simmer in my gentler body, and those were not times to remember. This time, I was ready to pay the fine.

"Now, Father," I said, "I did have the book out."

Father gave me a look. "I," he said grandly, "believe in the principle of a thing. You," he said, "are a member of the faculty. As such, you are entitled to take books out and keep them. I'll tend to it immediately."

Armed with the card, he bore down on Miss March the next morning. "You have made a mistake," he said. "My daughter received a notice with regard to a book."

Miss March must have been happy to have him at last. "Yes," she said, "the book is four weeks overdue."

"Since when," demanded Father, in a clarion voice, "do faculty members pay for time on books?"

Miss March said, "The rules for faculty members do not apply to graduate students."

Everybody in the library listened with interest. Father recalled every instance of Miss March's failure to file reference books on reference shelves, to locate missing volumes, to catalogue correctly. The whole library system was polished off in Father's style, which was vivid.

"Your daughter," said Miss March grimly, "owes us seventy-five cents."

[176]

THE ELMS ON THE CAMPUS

Father had a class and he left to teach it. But the next free period he was back, and they went all over it again. The whole question was whether I was a teacher primarily or a student. Teaching one class for one term did not make me a faculty member in Miss March's eyes.

Miss March sent me another notice. Father went back to the library. They argued through half a semester. I didn't dare get another book out while this was going on, and it was very trying for me.

The reluctant Northern spring came, and the elms on the campus gentled from winter austerity into April's mist. Grass grew, and the May Queen was being nominated.

But the real question was whether that seventy-five cents would or would not be paid. The president refused to settle it. He didn't want any more trouble with Miss March than he always had, and as for Father, he felt he could paddle his canoe and every other boat around with half a chance.

"Your daughter owes seventy-five cents," Miss March said.

Mamma was dreadfully humiliated. "All over such a little sum," she said, "stirring up all this furor!"

"I'll never pay it!" declared Father. "I'll resign first!"

Finally, I crept in and paid it. I was terrified for fear Father would find out and disown his weak-minded offspring, but I really hated to be shut out of the library.

Father was not speaking to Miss March, he tended to his own reserve shelves, and checked out his own volumes. When she stopped waylaying him to demand the money, he felt satisfied that he had won.

"She finally came to her senses," was the way he put it.

But he never forgot. Years later, long after she had gone

to her reward, Father would say, "Yes, I remember Miss March. She was the librarian who tried to charge faculty members for taking out books." He would add, "She made a mistake when she thought she could extort money from me!"

I never forgot that seventy-five cents either. I was more careful when I consulted Father over minor things.

One happening that put Miss March out of his mind at the time was the beginning of his battle with the City Gas and Fuel Company. The electric range was not yet on the market, although we had one of the new electric refrigerators at about this time. Or maybe I am wrong, perhaps the gas battle came when we still had the big round icebox and put the card in the window every morning for fifty or a hundred pounds of river ice brought by the Lutz ice wagon.

We had a gas stove. It was enormous, and had a top oven that almost reached the ceiling. We had a fireless cooker too, which was a metal box thing with a deep well and a heavy lid. You heated a pair of soap stones shaped like wheels and put them in and set the cooker pan in, closed the lid, and there you were.

The gas burners lighted with a match, flared up and then gave off a lusty smell of gas while cooking. The trouble with ours had to do with the pressure. Sometimes there was just enough to make a small fizzle and sometimes the flame blazed wildly. Usually when Mamma needed good pressure, there would be hardly enough to warm the water.

But in spite of this, the gas bills were terrific. And they kept rising every month. Father decided there was a leak somewhere in the main and he called the Gas Company and said so, firmly but politely.

A man came to check the stove and the pipes. He tramped in a lot of mud and got the kitchen very dirty and departed, whistling.

The next month the bill was higher. Father took it in his hands and charged out of the house and went to the main office.

A man came to check the stove and the pipes. Mamma cleaned up the kitchen.

The bill was higher. At this point if the whole main had exploded the extra noise wouldn't have been noticed around our house.

The company, embattled, now explained that our house was too far from the main supply and we just couldn't expect much pressure.

Father then refused to pay the bills. So a man came to check the stove. He said we needed a new stove. The old one leaked gas anyway. They had a new model on the floor in the office, he would send it down. Father said he was going to get a kerosene stove and never lay eyes on a gas man again.

The bill went down. Flushed with victory, and conscious of having saved his little family again from the wolves, Father went down cellar and stoked up the furnace.

It wasn't his fault he got the gasoline can instead of the oil can, and it was all very lucky for he only had his eyebrows and front curls singed off, and he was able to do over the cellar himself.

In these days when everybody has rights except the consumer, I like to think of Father and the Gas Company. There was a day when the individual could do battle successfully, a time when defective shirts even could be returned and your money refunded. Oh, golden era that has gone!

Now when it takes us six months to get a load of coal delivered, I sometimes wonder whether Father might still have achieved victory. I know the coal company would have been worn out at any rate.

Times were changing, however. The stock market was sound, and Father invested the income from Grandfather's estate, and prospered. The idea of diversified investment seemed safe to him, so he bought a share here and a share there. When the crash came later, Father lost nothing except on a few shares of woolen.

But when his own estate was settled, the lawyers nearly lost their minds trying to sort out the countless certificates. It took weeks.

Due to his canny operations with the market, Father did not have to live on the professor's salary, which was not much. He could buy one of the first victrolas, in dark mahogany and with a big cabinet underneath. It was a wonder. The old machines with their roll records and morning glory horns in blue and purple made music that sounded as if a crowd of tomcats had become involved inside somehow.

But our victrola sounded loud and clear. Father bought all of *Faust* and a lot of other opera music. (Caruso was his idol, he went to Chicago to hear him sing.) He had the Lucia sextette with all the great stars, the Lombardi trio, a lot of *Martha,* and Handel's *Largo.*

THE ELMS ON THE CAMPUS

But he didn't want any Wagner or German songs. He said
he didn't trust the Germans.

And he didn't want me to have any popular records. It
would give me a depraved taste in music. It wasn't safe.
Besides it was a waste of money. He was always very eco-
nomical about anything he didn't want, and he didn't like
popular music.

My friends cared absolutely nothing for Caruso or Alda
or Pol Plancon. Even *Hearts and Flowers* wasn't much of a
thing to dance to. But my allowance of twenty-five cents a
week didn't cover much music buying.

So we had another family crisis and it lasted long enough
for me to learn a lot of opera and develop a passionate taste
for the Good Night Quartette from *Martha* and *Lost,
Proscribed* and *Toreador Song* and so on. And then Father
indulged in *Pinafore,* since he had sung the lead in it in
college, so I learned all of *Pinafore.*

Meals were something of a nightmare to Mamma, standing between us, for I fought bitterly, because my social
standing was at stake. And I was in love with a boy who
wanted to dance to *Ivanhoe Two-Step* and not to the ballet
music from *Faust.*

In the end, Father let me buy *The Whistler and His
Dog.* I played it every minute that I was home, before
breakfast, at lunch, in the evening and before I went to
bed. I loved it. I still do. But Father got so sick of that infernal whistling that he told me for goodness sake to get
something else and I became the proud owner of *Ivanhoe
Two-Step,* followed subsequently by *Maple Leaf Rag, The
Old Green River, Moonlight Bay* and other perfectly rav-
ishing melodies. I also had a whole book of Hawaiian

[181]

records. Which is why, years later, when I heard Tommy Dorsey's rendition of *Hawaiian War Chant,* I cried out, "That's not a war chant! That's *Bubbling Spring!*" And there it was—*Kaua i ka huahuai.*

The second great purchase was the automobile. Father's was one of the first in town. He might have chosen a Cadillac, like our friends the Russells or a Carter Car like the Ritchies. He could have had a Stanley Steamer. But he wanted something different, so he bought a Keeton. It was the only one I ever saw, and the only one anywhere around our countryside. It was painted Brewster green, trimmed largely with brass and had a hood years and years ahead of its time for it was a long low slanting affair.

It was big enough for five people and an Irish setter, and there were side curtains to button on when it rained. The curtains had celluloid windows in them, through which you could hazily see the landscape race by at fifteen or twenty miles an hour.

Father loved it. Once we had the car, we never stayed home. At last, Father could go places again. The roads were fearful, but he racketed all over the country. Mamma, in long duster, goggles, hat and veil and cotton gloves, sat beside him, clinging to the door and saying, "Do go slower! Do go slower!"

I rolled around and bounced up to the ceiling in the back seat. Father's confidence in himself and his car was unbounded. He was always shooting down narrow dirt trails that ended in the deep woods. Old lumber roads long abandoned, lured him. We were half to the hubs in swamps, we slugged through sand, we got through cow tracks with the branches whipping the car on either side and the radiator steaming furiously.

A Sunday afternoon ride was permitted, since it wasn't really recreation. It was looking at nature's wonders. So every Sunday after church and a big chicken dinner, we got in the car and swooped away.

And then we went to the Dells. The Dells of the Wisconsin were like Mecca for the faithful. But to go via automobile was even better than taking the train. Father persuaded the Russells to make the pilgrimage with us, and their Cadillac followed along.

I suppose it takes a couple of hours or so to get to the Dells now, but it took three days for that excursion. We had both cars loaded with suitcases, robes, picnic hampers, coats and scarves, rubbers and umbrellas, and camera equipment.

Father was an avid picture-taker and he carried his large camera and the tripod and the box of plates everywhere. He wanted to make lantern slides for his class of the rock formation which made the Dells beautiful.

We got on the edge of town before the Russells had their first flat tire. Father and Mr. Russell jacked up the big Cadillac, perspiring freely in the hot summer sun, and got the tire changed. We started again, and went a few miles before we had to stop while Father bolted up to the farm well and filled his watering can for the radiator. We always went with an eye out for wells.

Five miles farther on, the Russells had another flat tire. Father got out and helped change it. It took a long time in those days, tires being difficult to get on and off. We were a little discouraged by the time we got started off again.

[183]

ESPECIALLY FATHER

Mr. Russell asked Father not to drive too fast. He thought the speed and the heat might be hard on the tires.

In the next town we hung around a couple of hours while the tires were vulcanized. And we got about ten miles outside of that town, when the Russells had another flat tire. Father was distinctly annoyed. We had our picnic lunch right on the edge of the dusty road to save time, with Father and Mr. Russell munching their chicken while working.

Bowling along in a cloud of dust, we made a few miles more, and then Father had to stop and fill our radiator again. The Russells didn't care, because they had another flat tire at that moment.

By the time we got to the Dells, we were so tired we could hardly enjoy them. Mr. Russell had left a couple of tires to be patched again, and we picked them up and went to Baraboo to spend the night. We had more hampers of food left, so we picnicked outside of town while Mr. Russell left a tire to be fixed.

The sky was soft and clear and it was faintly cooler. We spread the picnic on the bench beside an old race track and ate comfortably. Father told Mr. Russell he would be better off with a Keeton than that Cadillac. Then he gave a lecture on the Dells, which was very enjoyable.

The oldest Russell boy drove back to pick up the patched tires. Our troubles were over, we felt pretty good. After all, an automobile trip might be a little slow, but you weren't dependent on train schedules anyway.

The race track was a pretty oval in the gathering dusk, and the Russell boy came back from town and decided to drive around it a couple of times. He whisked past us the first time at about thirty miles an hour, and Mr. Russell stood up and waved his arms and shouted to him to stop. But he didn't hear, of course, and he drove by us again, in great triumph. Dust fanned out behind the car. He got the speed up to thirty-five.

And with a loud explosion, all four tires blew out.

The scene that followed is the kind one veils.

We spent the night in Baraboo and half the next day while the tires were being repaired. Father thought we never would get home, he was getting wild. And when at last we left the ill-fated Baraboo behind, he gunned the motor considerably.

"Thank goodness," he said, "we're on our way for the last time!"

"Mr. Russell is blowing his horn," I said meekly.

Father uttered his worst profanity. "Confound it, what's he want now?"

But he had to stop. Mr. Russell said, "We'll have to go back to Baraboo."

"What for? Why in heaven's name go back?"

"Well, I left my watch under the pillow in the hotel," said Mr. Russell.

We went back.

Home looked like a haven to Mamma and me. We were blistered with sunburn and windburn, and sand had reddened my eyes even with the black smoked goggles. Mamma, who bruised easily, had several black and blue marks from unexpected flingings about.

The Russells were glad to get back too. They had had

thirteen flat tires in the three days, and it was some time before they went outside the city limits again in their car.

"I am certainly thankful to be safe at home," said Mamma, unwinding her long veil. "I don't see as the Dells are worth all the advertising they get, anyway. They're not a bit lovelier than the Fox river right below our own dam."

"Well, let's get unpacked," said Father, "and put everything right where we can get it for next weekend."

"What about next weekend?"

"I thought we might run up to Waupaca," said Father, "and take a look at those chain-of-lakes formations." He added, "It's a nice drive."

Mamma sighed. She had a premonition of the kind of life she would be leading from then on. A car, Mamma felt, was a mixed blessing.

About this time, Father began to make hurried trips to look at gold mines, oil well prospects, artesian water supplies. He went all over the country and to Canada. His reputation grew until it got so a number of business men wouldn't invest in a stock until Father had looked over the holdings and assured them that there was something there.

The artesian wells were drilled usually for big paper companies that needed pure water and tons of it. Father always got it, but our lives were ordered by the time before the well came in when Father was irritable and jumpy, and the day the well came in when we could have almost anything we wanted. If a well driller lost a tool in the bottom of the drill hole, life was not worth living at home.

There was, I thought, a kind of fate in this expanding relationship between Father and the paper mills. It was as if the family of which he was such an independent branch, reached out to draw him back to the world of paper making. He went East and covered miles of ground studying the rock outcroppings, following the great frozen folds of rock strata, and measuring with his steel tape.

"There is water here," he would say. "You will strike it at a hundred and four feet."

And when at a hundred and three and a quarter feet the drillers pulled the bit out, there was the water, maybe three hundred gallons a minute, gushing pure and unspoiled from the deep earth.

"My well," Father would say. "She's a good one."

It was always his well, though the company had the use of it. He was amiable about letting them have the water, but woe to the company that damaged it in any way. Once or twice someone drilled another well for supplementary water and drew off the water from Father's well.

They heard from Father.

Now and then, a smart well driller would try to get away with a twelve-inch instead of a sixteen-inch diameter hole. Or was careless about losing the diamond drill. Or failed to take samples at each new strata. Smoke from these encounters drifted back home.

Once or twice sleek and elegant men came to call about a gold or silver mine somewhere in the West, and finding the little professor mixing cement in a wheelbarrow for some project around the yard, felt they were really in luck.

It was odd that so many well-heeled men around the state had to have his recommendation before buying stock, but it would be easy to get it. I don't blame them, Father had such an innocent look and his bright blue eyes were candid and open. His clothes were shabby and forever out of press because the minute he got in them, they gave up. The knees of his trousers belled out like circus balloons. He moved fast, he sat down swiftly, and he never in his entire life pulled up a single trouser leg the way some "silly" men did. Buttons popped from his shirts, ink splashed on his cuffs. He loved beautiful materials, he loved all fine things. He would buy the most expensive imported goods, and have them tailor-made. They sometimes did not fit perfectly because he hated so to stand still while the tailor measured, but they were good suits.

But by the time the mine promoters came to see him, they didn't look like much.

His shoes were like the shoes of a mill laborer. The laces might be broken and tied up again, there was usually paint on the toes, various bits of muddy soil, and his rapid bounding walk ran the heels down.

He wore red and blue ties no wider than a string, and they hiked up toward one ear. But a beautiful diamond tie pin rode crookedly on the tie of the month.

Smiling easily, the callers would advance their proposition. Father would get a nice percentage for recommending the mine, and it wasn't necessary for him to take the long trip to look at it. He could just sign the report from their own mineralogist, who was a great expert.

"I never sign my name to anything," Father would say, standing with his feet a little apart, his head back, "unless it's my work."

"But this is a mere technicality," the voice was smooth, "I feel sure you would agree . . ."

"I'll look at your property," Father would say, "at my

usual rate. I'll report just what is there. And I'll take no percentages on anything. If you decide, put it in writing and mail it to me."

They might try to talk him into it. Then Father would throw them out, and go back to his cementing.

Once a gold mining company sent him out to Nevada or somewhere beyond my horizon, evidently with the idea that a college professor from a small college wouldn't know much anyway and could be shown around by the right man, and give a glowing report.

Father, costumed like a prospector, appeared on schedule. He was shown about, handsomely fed, presented with sacks of lovely gold ore, and escorted back to the little hotel near the town. And the next morning around six, Father was back poking around himself and taking his own specimens of the ore and riding down in the cage. He wandered through the neighboring land too and drew his little pictures.

When he came home, he wrote a rather long report. And the company never released it. They had to pay Father, though. He had his written contract.

Then there was the discovery of oil in Wisconsin, right near home.

Everybody was excited, dreams of wealth burgeoned like June peonies. People looked at their own back yards with hope. Stock was going to sell like hotcakes, and a new era of prosperity set in for the Badger state.

"Nonsense," said Father. "There's no oil coming in there."

For once, it seemed he was wrong. He went down to the location and the digging was under way. There was oil in the well, seeping thickly into the opening. A muddy bluish scum formed around the edge of the well.

Father tested it. It was oil, all right, and it was coming into the hole of its own volition.

He came home, defeated. "But it oughtn't to be there," he said. "It's against all the natural laws of topography."

The owner was jubilant. Even the professor had to admit he found oil right there in the oil well.

"Never mind," said Mamma. "It's just happened one time."

But Father kept brooding. Then he got in the car and drove back. He made several trips. Meanwhile the digging went on, and people were daily more excited.

One Saturday Father got on his high boots and all the rest of the equipment, and took off, and was gone all day. When he came home, his face had that shining look of triumph.

"I've found their oil," he said.

"You mean it isn't in the well?" asked Mamma.

"Oh, it's there all right," grinned Father. "And it gets there all by itself. There just happens to be a garage not far away, and the garage man just happens to dump his waste oil behind the garage. And there just happens to be a dip in the land and sandy soil."

"Did you tell them so?"

"Certainly. But they wouldn't believe me. So," said Father, pulling off his boots, "they'll just go on digging up the waste oil from the garage. But they'll never make a well out of it. The garage can't do that much business."

And he was right. In a couple of weeks the oil well began to give nothing but muddy water filmed with oil, and eventually the driller pulled up and went on to better prospects, and only the open hole was left of the bonanza oil well.

Father was becoming reconciled to the quiet academic life, what with all these extras he was able to dig up, and he decided he might as well build a house. It was really too bad he couldn't build it entirely himself, but he couldn't. He wouldn't waste any money on an architect, though. And he bossed the men who did build it, and helped them.

"We'd get ahead a lot faster," one of them told Mamma, "if the Professor didn't help us so much."

It confused them too, that he kept changing his mind about the size and arrangement of rooms and other small details. The house was to stand on the brow of the hill going down to the river, and Father wanted it too near the edge. All the experts predicted it would slide down one sad day.

"It will never move an inch," said Father.

And by the time he was through with the foundation walls, the whole town might have vanished in an earthquake, and Father's house would have stood, unsinking, uncracked. Tons and tons of concrete were poured, and not a lean mixture either. Great buttresses were constructed, and as the house rose, it had the look of a fortress.

The minute we moved in, Father cast an eye at the hill, with its steep slope to the river. Too much erosion, he said. He ordered more cement. And then, singlehanded, he began a series of retaining walls on the slope.

Whenever anyone asked for him, Mamma would say, "He's down the hill, pouring cement."

Sometimes he hired a student to help, but nobody held out very long. The hill was as steep as a cliff, and tossing boulders around and setting forms was a very rugged form of exercise. And Father never let them sit down and rest either.

"Not worth a hill of beans," said Father, in disgust.

He was spending a small fortune on those bags of cement and the once-lovely slope looked like a gutted battlefield whence all but Father had fled. Mamma did all she could. She told him he was throwing money away. She told him he would kill himself. She told him he was ruining the hill. She told him they couldn't use that land for anything after he got through. And she told him he was driving her stark raving mad.

To all of these truths, Father said, "I'm going to fix that hill. I'll show you."

He planted some fruit trees down toward the bottom, after the lower wall was in place. And they grew good fruit too. But this was no blessing, for the little boys from all over town slipped along the river path and picked everything as fast as it got ripe, so Father was always charging at dangerous speed down the hill yelling and waving his arms. He threatened to shoot them. He strung barbed wire along the line.

There was never, said Mamma, one single quiet moment.

Then he decided to raise watermelons, because he loved watermelons with a great and lasting love. He paid absolutely no attention to the fact that the short Northern summer was against watermelon culture.

He spent a lot of money on fertilizer, hoes and spades and rakes. He bought manure and worked it in, coming up to meals smelling decidedly like a stable.

If it was dry, he lugged buckets of water down that perilous descent.

And in the end, one year, he raised one small pale watermelon. He came up the hill, dripping with sweat, very dirty, and the little melon cradled in his arms. It was about the size of an acorn squash and it was a delicate spring green.

"There you are!" he said, laying it on the table. "I told you I was going to raise watermelons!"

Mamma divided it in three for dessert for supper. We each ate a small wedge. Inside it had plenty of slippery black seeds, but only a little light pink flesh. And it was rather rubbery.

Father ate his, and then laid down his fork and pushed the hard rind away. "I ought to sue those seed people," he said. "If they can't put out better seeds than this, they ought to go out of business."

With beans, he had better luck. He sowed several packets, believing if a little was good, more was always better. The beans came in. Mamma spent a whole summer trying to stem the tide of beans that flowed in the back door. There were bushels of beans. We ate beans twice a day as long as we could. We gave beans to all the beanless neighbors.

And we canned beans. Dozens and dozens of jars.

The summer seemed like a nightmare to me, because I was stringing beans day and night. I never could do anything until I had done the beans that day. Finally, when the beans stopped coming, Mamma almost cried with joy.

"That's all the thanks I get," said Father morosely, "for raising a good crop for you."

We were getting ready for a carload of company. They were coming for an indefinite stay, and I knew what that meant. When I thought of the dishwashing, I wished I had been born an orphan.

It was a sizzling-platter day when they drove up, the hottest of the year. Mamma and I went out and greeted them, and they poured into the house with tons of luggage. Father was nowhere to be seen, and Mamma said he had stepped out to do an errand.

While the guests were washing and unpacking, Mamma flew about the kitchen mashing potatoes, making gravy, buttering hot rolls, looking in the old gas oven at the pie.

I was setting the table, very gloomy.

Then the back door opened and Father burst in carrying a bushel basket. "The beans are in again!" he said.

And those particular guests spent their first day stringing beans. Mamma made Father string too, and with the company working, he had no way to escape. The beans were all saved, and the fruit cellar was stocked for eternity with rows and rows of jars.

And next summer, Father did not plant a single bean. "Peas are better," he said. "You don't string peas."

Father didn't like any of the textbooks that had been written for his courses. They were a waste of money and of time, he said. So he decided he would write one himself.

His scientific bulletins were excellent, he had a pile of published ones in his study that were so technical I couldn't even understand what they were about.

But the text was to be for elementary students. Father got embroiled with it early in the academic days, and as the years passed, the stack of manuscript overflowed his desk, bookcases, and the study.

There were two difficulties with his text. The first was that he wanted to put in everything he knew, and he knew a lot. He couldn't bear to leave out a single thing that he had learned in his years of study and travel. His introductory chapter covered the universe from the beginning to last Tuesday.

Excited by thinking of it, he composed pages and pages on any small point that came up. And if anyone suggested he leave out or condense or simplify, he was outraged.

"But that's interesting!" he would say.

This meant that he skipped around considerably. He did make outlines, but he never paid any attention to them for they cramped his freedom. He wrote by free association. You might find yourself one moment prowling the wastes with the dinosaurs which he adored, and the next minute mining for coal in Pennsylvania.

This was distracting for the average reader.

The second major difficulty was that his poetic nature crept out continually. You might not think geology and poetry would combine, but Father combined them.

His education in poetry was limited to Whittier, Longfellow, Burns, and Felicia Hemans, or the Greeks. So he tossed in tidbits of them at random, liking the sound of the words. His whole style was colored by the best Victorian phrasing on this account.

"And the desert shall blossom like the Rose of Sharon," he would say, when he was talking about the effect of irrigation.

It wasn't what you would call textbook style.

When I was old enough to realize, I felt very sad to think of the wealth of knowledge which a good collaborator could have organized and which only frightened publishers. But nobody could collaborate with Father. He wanted appreciation, and not criticism. Once or twice I edited a few pages and when the smoke of battle died down, Father simply copied back in all his flights of fancy and all the pleasant irrelevant things he had thought about.

It was a great pity, for a whole library could have been stocked from Father's knowledge.

His lectures did not make a book either. When Father finally became group-minded enough to be a Rotarian, he began to give talks for all kinds of clubs all over the state. As a lecturer, he was highly successful, for he could talk without being pinned down to his notes, and if he fell into a mood of technical terms, people just waited until that part was over.

But when the lectures were assembled, they were very much like the ill-fated textbook. A combination of deep scientific knowledge and poetry quotations did not add up to a volume with any consistency.

This was a pity too, for people still remember the lecture called *Six Miles Under the Sea*. In this one, you took an imaginary walk on the bottom of the sea with Father leading the way from New York to England. You saw everything there was, too, from the tiniest crushed fossil form under your feet to the deepest deep-sea denison oozing past you in the great dark.

Also, being with Father, you found buried ships with pirate's gold spilling from them and jewels "a king's ransom." Often this would remind him of a few facts about pirating which he would toss in briskly.

Another memorable lecture was called *The Role of Un-*

derground Water in Human Affairs, and feeling the way he did about underground water this flowed with energy and fancy.

He had some extra time to work on the sheaf of lectures the winter he had his accident. The textbook was laid aside for the time being, he would go at it again after the lecture book was done. Neither of these projects defeated Father, he was held up by fate, he thought, but he would have the text and the lectures published eventually, and nothing ever made him lose faith in them.

We had a heavy snow that winter, and Father objected to a heavy snow on general principles. It was very cold, too, and he was always carrying boiling water out the back door to thaw out the car. This annoyed him.

"There's too much snow on the roof," he told Mamma, one Thursday as she was going off to Clio Club. "It isn't a good thing."

"It will go off in a day or so," said Mamma, with her mind on her book review.

"It ought to go off right now," said Father.

"Well, don't worry about it."

"I think I'll just get a ladder and go up there," he said, "and shovel it off."

Mamma stopped in the door. "Don't you dare try it!" she said. "Don't you even get out the ladder! In all this snow and ice—"

"It isn't safe to leave it," said Father obstinately.

"I don't care if it is or not," Mamma was stubborn too for once. "You stay off that roof. You'll fall off and break your neck!" And she gathered up her brown velvet bag, her long gloves, her beaver fur piece, and departed.

[197]

The minute she had rounded the corner of John Street, Father was whipping into his mackinaw. Surveying the situation carefully, he decided to save time by crawling out of the top story window in the front of the house. This would let him on the porch roof, from whence it was a mere step to the main roof.

Carrying his large and extra heavy snow shovel ("I want one that is good and sound," he said) he crawled out of the window. The roof had plenty of snow on it, all right, and some ice, and a good steep pitch. It was rather like a miniature ski-run up there, and as Father lifted the shovel for a first dig, he shot down like lightning with the shovel preceding him just fast enough so he could land on it.

I found him when I came home from school, and he was just regaining consciousness then. I started to scream.

"I can't get up," he said. "Stop that and help me in the house."

I went over, strangling on my screams, and tried to heave him up, but I couldn't manage the hundred and eighty or so that he then weighed, and all solid too. So, after a brief and painful struggle, Father said, "Go get the doctor. Tell him I fell off the roof."

The doctor came like a rocket. He was devoted to Father, and this time, he thought the end must have come. His face was as white as a clean sheet as he swung out of his car and banged up the walk with his black bag, his coonskin coat flopping wildly.

We got Father inside and laid on the couch and the doctor went over him carefully.

Father was fully conscious and very mad by now.

"What in the world were you *doing* up there?" asked the doctor.

"I simply went up to shovel a little," said Father.

Instead of breaking his neck or his spine or both legs, Father had merely smashed the heel of one foot. Otherwise he was in fine shape. An acrobat couldn't have done better.

"We'll have to put a cast on and you'll keep off it for a few weeks," said the doctor. "I guess this will keep you quiet for a little while."

"I've got a geology class at eight in the morning," said Father. "I can't just sit around at home."

Mamma came home then, and had a hard time between being glad he was still alive and mad about the whole thing.

"I told you so," she said. "I told you so."

"It wasn't my fault," said Father, "it was all the shovel. It pushed me."

This was the way he got extra time on the lectures.

Ills of the Flesh

FATHER DID NOT FIT INTO THE TYPICAL MOLD OF THE COL-
lege professor, the gentle, thinnish rather under-colored
man with thick glasses and an odd haircut. Preoccupation
with things of the mind generally leads to absent-mindedness, an academic tread, and sober clothing.

The fever for keeping fit had not swept the country, so
the professors went about their duties growing more
stooped, and breathing chalk dust incessantly and having
trouble with their eyes from too much night reading.
Stomach trouble was common, two or three of the men had
severe ulcers, heart trouble was a familiar ailment, and
pneumonia struck hard and often. Everybody had grippe
in the long sunless winters.

Exercise consisted in volley ball for the younger members
of the faculty, for the Country Club was patronized chiefly
by paper mill executives and young socialite couples. A
professor raising a family, studying in vacations, rarely had
any money to spend on anything like golf. In later years,
a few of them joined, but mostly for little dinners and card
games.

The average professor had a frail look, like a plant raised
in a cellar. Underpaid and overworked, they hurried across

the campus with heads bent and armloads of books under their arms.

But Father, however, was healthy. He was made of something like welded steel. And there was nothing sedentary about his life.

He rose at five-thirty or six, making so much noise that nobody else in the house could sleep. He was lonesome until Mamma got up. So he pounded and sawed things, or mowed the lawn under the bedroom windows, or cleaned the furnace.

At seven-thirty he dashed off for an eight o'clock class, and he never was one of the weaklings that wanted nine o'clock to start the day. You had to get busy, he thought, or you wasted your time.

He taught all morning, ran home for a quick lunch, taught or had field trips all afternoon, bounced home for six o'clock supper, then either studied or corrected papers all evening unless there was a faculty meeting.

Weekends he took the car to pieces, or cemented something, or chopped firewood, or hung storm windows, or dug up the hillside furiously and moved stones around.

He went hunting whenever the season was on, rising in the middle of the night to take off for a faraway place where the hunting was always better than it was near home. Fishing was too slow, too much time sitting in a boat.

Some of his excess energy went into faculty meetings which were always violent. But they fought sitting down in wooden armchairs. These battles were over such questions as whether the college flag could be properly raised at half-mast when the president's mother died. The physics man claimed it was setting a dangerous precedent, for if the flag were lowered everytime a parent of the staff died, it would never be aloft at all. The Latin man said the president's mother was in a special category. Father said the flag ought to be hauled down and left down, it was a nuisance.

The meeting lasted three hours.

There was another over the size of bluebooks for examinations, and there were annual ones over extending the Christmas vacation another day if the last day fell on Friday. Should the students have an extra long weekend or was it a bad precedent to set?

It is easy, has always been easy, to make fun of the childlike qualities of teachers, especially college professors. They are childlike. But then, as now, they were the ones to keep the life of the mind important in a world of much materialism. Things of the spirit were theirs and they seldom forsook them.

Possibly it was partly because they gave their strength so completely to the job of battering down the ignorance of the youngsters that they lacked a little balance with regard to simple things like the bluebook size or the vacation day.

They worried about their health. Vitamins had not swamped the country then, hormones and sulfa and penicillin were unheard of, but there were plenty of cures for almost any pain a professor might feel.

The Hay diet came in. The psychology professor took it up. The basis of the Hay diet was that foods one normally ate did not mix comfortably in the stomach. I never understood it, although we had all the literature.

"It will kill him," predicted Father darkly, "and kill his poor wife too. They eat sliced apples and milk for breakfast.

Hay diet. All right for cows to live on hay, but not for people!"

Father expressed his views frankly and honestly whenever he was with the dieters. "There's no reason for them to be offended," he said. "I am just telling them the truth about this fad."

A rift developed between psychology and geology. Mamma told him to stop talking about it.

"I thought they had some sense," retorted Father, "but any time you see me go to a faculty dinner with parched corn in my pocket for my dinner, send for the police and have me locked up!"

Whatever was wrong with anyone, Father thought a good square meal was called for. Any kind of special diet indicated a weak mind. And as for eating starch and protein separately, who ever heard of such nonsense?

Father took care of his own health in what he considered the only sensible way. He kept his strength up by three square meals a day and a few snacks in between, and he dosed himself with patent medicines if he came down with a cold.

He did succumb now and then to a head cold, which he called Coryza. When he had Coryza, his eyes ran and his nose ran and his temper was dreadful.

He used two methods of combatting it. The first was exercise. He would sally forth in a blizzard or a heavy rain and clean out the gutters or shovel a little cement.

Secondly, he dosed. He never thought of consulting a doctor. He made his own diagnosis on the theory that he knew what was wrong with himself better than anyone else.

He dosed himself when he was perfectly well too, just

as a preventive. There was a whole shelf in his bathroom filled with bottles and boxes. And if there happened to be any pills lying around that anyone else was taking, Father would try a few of those too.

Before going to bed at night, he fortified himself from the ills of the flesh by a good beaker of bromo seltzer. Then he ate a sandwich with sliced Bermuda onion in it. He liked patent tonics too, especially if they had a malt base.

In the morning he took Sal Hepatica, and followed with a small breakfast of hot cereal and cream, bananas, bacon and eggs, coffee, and hot muffins or toast.

When Father had a very severe cold, with a temperature, nothing would induce him to stay in bed a day. He took rhinitis and sprayed his nose vigorously with an oil spray. Mamma gave up rubbing his chest with goose grease and laying flannel on, for he only thought of something to do outdoors and rushed out when he was all greased up and steaming.

His eyes were no trouble. He did the most minute microscopic work with no glasses, and he could see a pin across the room. It wasn't until he was, I think, sixty-five that he had to wear glasses for fine reading and he was outraged. Mamma was not very sympathetic about his eyes, she couldn't see to thread a needle without glasses for years.

When Mamma became seriously ill, and had to go to the Mayo Clinic, Father went along too. This was when he was well up in late middle age—if you could think of him being anything but young. Maybe there was something the matter with him, he thought, suddenly. He couldn't run as fast as he used to, nor lift as big rocks.

He had some symptoms which alarmed him, and he

diagnosed his ailment as cancer of the kidneys. For once he said nothing at all about fresh air and exercise and even his bromo seltzer left him insecure.

Besides he was right there anyway in Rochester and it was a saving of money to get something out of the trip except just Mamma's being gone over.

So Father went through the clinic too.

They told him he was the healthiest man of his age that they had ever laid eyes on. The only thing they could find was that he was overweight, he might cut down.

"Why, I don't eat much," said Father in surprise, "I only eat a small breakfast, and a little lunch, and not much dinner."

He ate, he felt, just exactly right. The doctors had to say something to get their money's worth. He went right on eating as he always had, and managed to keep his strength up very well.

In fact, he is the only man I ever heard of who at a rather advanced age would walk from Macy's in New York to West 111th Street because it was silly to take a cab and the air was bad in the subway. He said he got a little tired toward the end of the last mile but he had picked up a couple of bargain rugs on the way so it was worth it. This was when he visited me for a rest.

Father liked everything edible, except tearoom food. Wild horses could not drag him to a tearoom to throw away good money for a dab of pale chicken and a lettuce leaf.

The only thing he would not eat was mushrooms. Mushrooms were poisonous fungi, he said, and he wouldn't poison himself. If other people were fools, he couldn't help it, but he exercised good judgment in what he put in his stomach.

I adored mushrooms from childhood on, and when I was married, I had a semblance of independence and dared to eat them. Father would watch me with his face heavy with foreboding, lips pressed taut. For hours after the meal, he would wait for me to be stricken, and I may say my stomach always felt uneasy when he gave me that look of expected doom.

I used to wonder whether he would be glad if I did succumb because his theory would be proved correct or if he would be sorry! Someday, he said, after each crisis had passed, I would eat one of the Angels of Death and find out how foolish I was.

Father's sound eating and sensible medications, plus the fresh air rushing constantly into his lungs, and the strengthening exercise of hauling rocks, mixing cement, or putting on seventy-two storm windows unaided, kept him at a peak.

And he might no longer be the lean rangy figure of the early days, but his two hundred pounds could move faster than a hurricane wind.

Nevertheless, the time came when we almost lost him.

He had a bad attack of Coryza in the middle of the winter. He sprayed and took pills and ate plenty of onions. But he was pretty busy, and it was thirty below. He kept on making trips of twenty or thirty miles to neighboring towns on business, pleased at being the only man to drive instead of weakly riding the train.

His Coryza grew worse and his throat got sore. Very sore. He gargled so constantly that it sounded as if we had a small private waterfall in the bathroom.

He complained that it hurt him to eat. He did not care for a liquid diet, but steak and roast beef and French fried potatoes were hard to swallow.

This went on for several days. Finally he consented to have the doctor come, to swab out his throat with silver nitrate. Father was pretty mad about the whole thing, but Mamma kept nagging at him so he didn't have a minute's peace. He made this plain.

The doctor had a hard time getting him to open his mouth wide enough for anyone to look in his throat. It hurt, and Father didn't want to be hurt. He gagged, and snapped his mouth shut.

The doctor got it open again. Father snapped shut. But after a time, the doctor did get a quick glance down in that throat and he sat back and eyed the patient firmly.

"You've got to have your tonsils out," he said. "I never saw a worse set in my whole medical career."

"I don't believe in it," said Father, choking. "I don't know what the Lord put them there for if it's just to jerk them out."

"Well, they have to come out," said the doctor. "It's a very simple operation, takes no time at all, and you'll get over these bad colds."

Father was horrified at the idea. "I just have a cold," he said. "That's the trouble with you medical men, you want to cut people up all the time."

"As a matter of fact," said the doctor, "I don't like to take tonsils out, it's not my field. We'll get Dr. Brown, he's very fine."

"I wouldn't take a sick cat to him," said Father firmly. "I don't like the fellow. He smokes like a chimney and he charges too much."

"Then we'll get Dr. White."

"But I don't want my tonsils out," said Father.

"I am afraid you're going to have to," said the doctor.

Father finally gave in, because he had such a bad throat he couldn't stand it. The catch then was that when the acute stage had gone and the operation could be done, Father felt better enough so he thought the whole thing was unnecessary.

Mamma was worn to a frazzle by the time she got him packed up. If he'd been going to have his entire machinery overhauled, she said, he couldn't have made any more fuss.

At the last moment, Father decided that he wouldn't go to the hospital after all. He saw no reason why he couldn't just drop down to the doctor's office and get the tonsils yanked out there. Mine were disposed of that way.

"It's one thing with a child," said the doctor. "But at your age, you'll have to go to the hospital."

"There," said Father. "I knew it. It's dangerous."

"No, it isn't," said the doctor, "but it is much easier in the hospital."

"I can't stand hospitals," said Father fiercely. "And I won't have those nurses and nuns hanging over me."

The only hospital we had was the Catholic one, and it was a very fine hospital. But Father said a hospital was full of germs and if he caught something fatal, Mamma would be sorry.

He went off with the air of a French lord riding in a tumbril. He had plenty of luggage, enough in fact to provide for a long trip. He was only to stay one night at the hospital but he had several of his own night shirts. He did not intend to wear those hospital shifts. Also he tucked in his favorite medicines and several scientific bulletins to read.

It was pretty trying for Mamma and me. He had an air of noble martyrdom as we left him, implying that we had thought this all up as a persecution for him, and that he was a poor defenseless soul.

And my first view of him afterward confirmed my suspicion that perhaps he was right, and we had finished him.

One of the sisters was changing his ice pack. Father was screwed up in a miserable knot on the hard high hospital bed. He suffered the ignominy of a hospital gown, and all of his own things were out of sight. His face was white, his eyes desperate.

When he saw me in the doorway, he tried to rise up in bed, and he uttered a fierce croak, which made him cough violently.

"Stop it!" said the sister firmly, and she pushed him back flat on the bed and pressed the ice bag on his throat.

"You mustn't talk, Papa," I said nervously.

He eyed me like a trapped eagle. He waved the sister away. He coughed hard and gagged heavily, but he persisted in trying to clear his throat.

"Be quiet," said the sister. "You'll start the bleeding."

"Just lie quietly, Papa," I begged.

He gave a louder croak, and waved one arm. "It hurts," he said thickly.

"You may stay five minutes," the sister said to me, and she gathered up her tray and vanished with a ruffle of petticoats. The door being closed, Father began to clear his throat again. I was frightened. I begged him to be quiet, and this enraged him. He thrashed around in the bed, and muttered painfully.

"Killing me in this place," he said. "Get home. Must get out."

The doctor had to come in and threaten him. If he didn't quiet down, he said, the doctor would not be responsible for what happened. This quieted Father briefly while he thought over the idea that the operation had been bungled and he was going to die anyway.

If he were going to die, he wanted to depart life in a Methodist institution. At this point, the Mother Superior visited him and told him it was up to him to stop coughing and lashing about, and that no matter what religion he had, he was slowing up his recovery *himself*.

As a result of his struggles, Father had to stay in the hospital almost a week. My respect for the sisters was immense. I think secretly they liked nursing a fighter.

Finally he came home, riding as a passenger with the doctor, wrapped to the eyebrows in scarves and mufflers. The neighbors dropped in to congratulate him on his successful operation.

"Thought I was done for," Father said, choking. "Never let them jerk out your tonsils. Never."

The doctor advised him to keep quiet another day or so, and not to lecture all day long when he went back to college until his throat was thoroughly healed.

But father could not keep his mouth shut. He didn't care for lounging around either. He shook down the furnace, shoveled coal, ran up and down stairs incessantly, and wore Mamma out.

And when we sat down to eat, he would eye the soft food on his plate, turn away, sigh heavily, and reproach Mamma.

"It was all an awful mistake," he said.

He remembered the experience always. Let some innocent dinner guest start on the story of his or her operation
for gall bladder, ulcers, kidney stone, appendicitis.

Father's tonsil operation was more serious, more dreadful.

Let someone describe a bout with pneumonia, broken
legs, concussion, or tropical fever.

Father's tonsil operation was worse.

And he always managed to imply that it was a conspiracy
on the part of Mamma, the doctor and me. It was all our
fault that he had to undergo his horrible experience.

Of course it was.

When he had really recovered and gone back to his regular schedule, Mamma went to bed with an attack of grippe.
She had it by herself, very quietly, with no commotion, the
way she always had.

She never wanted to bother anybody.

On this occasion, I think she enjoyed the rest. Father
wouldn't disturb her, in case he might catch it on top of
his "weakened condition."

"In my weakened condition," he said, "I might get anything."

He fortified himself with a good shot of bromo seltzer,
some rhinitis, and a mammoth Bermuda onion sandwich.

"The trouble with your mother is," he said to me, "she
needs to get out and get some fresh air and exercise."

I knew better than to suggest he was inconsistent in his
health views.

I merely had an onion sandwich myself. Just to keep my
strength up.

10

Pomp and Circumstance

AS THE PRESS OF COLLEGE WORK INCREASED DURING THE year, Father would become a little more absent-minded than usual. Not that he ever admitted it. He never thought any of the jokes about absent-minded professors had any point, nor any validity.

Nothing made him madder than any remark about his forgetting that there was a special meeting for the faculty, and spending the time mixing cement for the garage drive. On the other hand, he always thought forgetting was its own excuse for any lapse.

"Where were you yesterday at five?" someone would ask.

"Oh, I forgot all about it," Father would say, blushing a little, but not at all regretful.

"It doesn't flatter people," Mamma would say in despair, "if they think you just don't care enough to try to remember!"

"Well, I can't help it if I forgot all about it," Father would say crossly.

Mamma did the best she could. She made engagement lists and crossed dates off calendars and wrote notes to Father and stuck them by his favorite stuffed blowfish on the desk.

Father would answer the phone when he was working on a report, and happily promise that we would all go somewhere on Saturday night. Then he would hang up the receiver and go back to his work, and never mention the call to Mamma.

Or he would say when Mamma came in, "Somebody called you, but I forgot what it was about."

"Who called?"

"Let me see, it was either Mrs. Gresham or Mrs. Burke, at least I think so. I was busy."

Keys were a constant pitfall.

Father had a small windowless darkroom at the college where he developed his plates and printed his pictures. He always locked the door when he entered, for otherwise some student would stick his head in and ruin the film. The trouble was that the door could not be unlocked from the inside without the keys, although you could lock it by pushing a little metal plunger thing.

So Father would lock himself in and work a couple of hours, by which time all the air was exhausted and he was dripping with perspiration. He would decide to go out and get some air, and then discover his keys were in his office on the desk.

The first time this occurred, he beat on the door for some time and shouted and pounded on the floor, but nobody happened to be passing by. Father was agile, and in the end, he climbed up and skinned through the transom and dropped down outside.

After this when he locked himself in, he never tried to summon help. He just mounted the sink and squeezed out of the transom.

Mamma said professors ought not to have keys.

Another little difficulty he had was with the car. He

would drive uptown to do errands and park somewhere around the corner from College Avenue. He was always careful to fix the doors so they would lock when he got out, just in case someone should steal the buffalo robe.

But he was not so careful about the keys, and sometimes he came back to the car loaded with bundles and found the car locked tight, and the keys inside on the dashboard.

The garage man would have to come and use a long thin wire which he ran up under the ventilator and with which, after considerable time, of course, he could open the door.

The set of duplicate keys did not help much, for they were always mislaid. Father might call up and order Mamma to send the extra keys to him at the drugstore, and this gave Mamma a nice morning of hunting. By the time she located them, Father would be home.

But this was not all the trouble. He would go off to town in a hurry, park the car and lope around doing his errands. He might go to the bank and spend half an hour deciding whether to buy one share of United Fruit or one of Bethlehem Steel.

Then he would come out and catch a ride home with a neighbor who was just driving by the bank.

Mamma would hear the car drive up, and see Father getting out of the neighbor's car waving a cheerful good-bye.

"Did you have an accident?" she would ask fearfully.

"Certainly not," Father would say. "Why should I?"

"Then what happened to the car?" Mamma would ask.

Father would start nervously, think rapidly, clap his hat on his head and dart away. He would walk back the two miles to town, trying to remember where he parked the car.

"I just forgot all about it," he would say, when he came home the second time.

Or he might drive to college in the morning if he were late for his eight o'clock, and park behind the gym. The parking lot was out of sight from the main campus, and when he emerged from the science building with his arms full of books, there was nothing to remind him that he had a car there.

He would come home, rush in to see what was for lunch, dump his load and then say breathlessly, "Oh, I've got to go back. I forgot something."

Mamma would put the meat loaf in the warming oven and keep the biscuits hot while he trotted back and retrieved the car. He never wanted to wait until he had eaten —he felt he'd better go right back and bring the car home.

It was hard on Mamma, and she didn't feel comforted when it appeared that I was like Father in his absent-mindedness. I was always promising to be in two places at once, or losing my locker key or leaving my library books in the streetcar. And I had no excuse, for presumably I was not using my mind on scholarly activity anyway.

Father had absolutely no patience with me. "Why don't you keep your mind on what you're doing?" he would snort. "You are too careless," he would say, "you'd lose your head if it weren't fastened on."

If Mamma had a headache, she would say, "She just takes after you."

Now when I pay the rent twice, or subscribe three times to the same magazine in one week, or locate the key to the safety deposit box in a pile of old letters. I always hear Mamma's comment, "She takes after you."

Mamma did almost all of the shopping, but when the mood to buy overtook him, Father would tell her to make out a list and he would get everything she needed at once.

He invariably lost the list on the way, but he would come home with the car laden.

"Did you bring the soap powder?" Mamma would ask.

"No, I forgot all about it," Father answered. "But I got a case of grapefruit. They were having a sale. Nice big cans."

"Mrs. Novak is waiting for the soap powder," Mamma would say. "She can't wash curtains with cans of grapefruit."

Rubbers, umbrellas, hats, gloves, scarves, notebooks, these were all things Father shed as he progressed rapidly about town.

Sometimes he would even wear one shoe of one pair and one of another when he dressed in a hurry with his mind on the fossil formations in a piece of shale.

Mamma inspected him whenever she could before he left the house.

"You've forgotten your tie," she would say. Or, "You need the dark coat with those pants."

But she couldn't always check on everything.

I remember vividly the occasions when they had to go to a formal dinner or a reception. These usually came on Saturday nights, and Father would be lugging rocks or making cement or working on the hillside all day. Or washing the car, or putting on storm windows, or cleaning the gutters. Almost anything that would wear him out by dusk.

Mamma would begin early to collect his wearing apparel. She knew how he hated to dress, and how tired he would be, and she tried to ease the situation.

His long underwear was laid on the bed in the big bed-room. Clean socks, the best shoes which hurt his tender feet, the stiff shirt—Mamma would take a clean collar from its cardboard support, hunt up a handkerchief which wasn't stained with acid.

The gold nugget tiepin was in the strawberry cushion on the dresser.

Finally at the last minute, Mamma would persuade Father to leave his work and come in for a hot bath. She would start the water running, and spread out the bathmat and the towels.

He was always hungry by then, and he wanted a snack before his bath. If they were going for dinner, he fussed because the hour was so late. Sensible people sat down to eat at six o'clock, and nothing later was any good at all. A person could starve waiting around for a seven o'clock meal.

Father taking a bath sounded like the break in some big power dam. Mamma would be downstairs brushing his coat when he came out, and long feathers of steamy air drifted down from the bathroom.

There would be bangings, pulling out of drawers, slamming of doors, and muttered exclamations from above as Father wrestled with dressing.

"Where are my studs? I can't find my studs!" he would roar.

"They're right there," Mamma would call back.

"No, they aren't. You've hidden them somewhere. I can't find them."

Mamma would fly upstairs.

There would be more banging around, and then the triumphant discovery that the studs were in the hand painted collar button holder where they belonged.

Flushed and perspiring, Father would come down at last, looking very handsome to us all, but with a martyred look in his blue eyes.

Mamma had to be ready. If she spent five minutes extra dusting rice powder on her straight little nose, Father would get restless and bolt down cellar to shake down the furnace, and cover himself with a fine film of ashes.

When they finally went out, I would watch them go down the steps, Mamma in her toast-colored lace and her velvet wrap, and Father with his white scarf billowing behind him, his black coat open, his shoes squeaking a little, as his best ones always did.

There was the smell of lavender and of Father's toilet water, and often it was quite strong—Father adored good smelling perfume and toilet water and slapped them on with a free and easy hand. There were times when his handkerchief would almost asphyxiate anyone if he took it out to mop his forehead.

He always came running back for his wallet or the keys, and then the car roared as he drove down the street, hurrying so they would be the first ones there.

Sometimes Mamma went out alone to Clio Club meeting. Father felt a little injured, left behind by himself. I was always off somewhere on a date, and he didn't like that much either.

He was a sound sleeper, and one night when she left him, he decided to go to bed early instead of waiting up for her.

Mamma came home, in due time, and found the house locked up tight. She was a little surprised, but she reached in her purse for her key, and discovered that it was in her other purse. So she had to ring the bell.

Nobody answered, so she rang again, pressing a small firm cold thumb on the brass button. It was a bitter winter night, and she began to shiver as she stood there, wondering why Father was so slow.

She rang the bell again. She rang it as hard as it would ring. She could hear it echoing in the house. She was afraid the neighbors would hear it.

Then she went around and rang the back doorbell.

There was no answer. After awhile she waded through the snow to the other side of the house and stood under the sleeping porch window. She yelled for Father. Mamma couldn't whistle, but she had a strong voice, and she shouted loudly and banged on the side of the house.

They always kept the windows of the sleeping porch open, even when it was below zero, for in those days fresh air was respected. But there was no answering shout from upstairs, and when her voice had given out, Mamma gave up, and went next door and waked the neighbors.

She phoned Father from there, and the operator sympathetically rang and rang and rang. Mamma hung up and tried again in five minutes, but nobody answered.

In the end, Mamma had to walk seven or eight blocks to the house of the family doctor who kept a set of keys for an emergency. She woke the doctor's family and got the keys and trudged back home again.

She let herself in, took off her snowy wraps, went upstairs to the sleeping porch, and Father sat up in bed.

"Well, there you are," he said crossly, "I thought you'd never come home. I haven't been able to sleep a wink!"

What Mamma said has never been recorded.

Mamma always kept track of when Father was to speak in chapel. He disliked this so violently that he was very apt to forget it. His turn came around inevitably some morning when his last excuse was used up. The college had a fine new chapel, with a good organ and expensive stained glass windows, but Father did not like to speak there.

He refused to pray or deliver a sermon, although he always tucked in a few morals with his talks about geology. He would sit stiffly frowning while the service began, then bound to his feet and speak rapidly.

The time he really held the students spellbound was the day that he had just begun his talk when the congregation was suddenly increased by our Irish setter, Timmie. Down the long aisle Timmie walked sedately, mounted the platform, and sat down beside Father, his tail waving and his eyes earnest.

Father ignored him. Timmie sat there, looking calmly at the auditorium, and now and then waving his tail as if he found something very good in the address. When the talk was over, Father and Timmie retired together and the students burst into applause.

Timmie took several courses in geology after that, and became a familiar figure trotting along the campus and going into Science Hall. He liked to come out with Father carrying a rolled newspaper or a pair of gloves.

Father saw nothing odd in the fact that Timmie could talk on the telephone—or at least listen over it. Timmie used to pay social calls on various friends, and when it was time for him to leave, his host would ring Father up and say, " Timmie is here."

"Call him to the phone," Father would direct.

The receiver would be placed against Timmie's ear, with his red silky ear folded back.

"Timmie, you come on home now," Father would say.

Timmie would jump down, rush to the front door, and run straight home. On one of these occasions, he came home with a toy telephone tied to his collar.

"So he can give you a ring himself," said the neighbor.

One sad day Timmie went under a barn after a rabbit and got stuck there. Father had to be called to come and dig him out, and when Timmie saw the shovel coming in, he squirmed around and pushed dirt up on it himself. People thought this was amazing, but Father only said Timmie ought to know better than get himself stuck in the first place.

But a reporter came from Milwaukee to write up the professor's dog. Mamma was proud, but Father said it was nonsense.

He did not really like most pets. Timmie was the only exception. In later years, when I acquired a cocker, Father said severely, "You better get rid of it. It isn't good to have an unsanitary animal around."

Cats he had little use for. They carried germs. One summer I ventured to have a small grey kitten, and Father gave her away to some people who stopped in to call. I was out at a party, and when I came home my kitten was on the way to Chicago.

He couldn't understand why I was heartbroken. She would have a good home, he said, the people seemed to like her.

I hoped he would mellow on the subject of my cocker,

but she was a smart dog, and she knew the minute she laid eyes on Father that he boded no good. So she bit him every time she could sneak up from the rear.

"But you loved Timmie," I said.

"Timmie was different. Timmie was a good dog."

He had gotten himself into the purchase of Timmie without meaning to. He offered me a graduation present when I finished school that year, and said handsomely I should have whatever I wanted.

I wanted a dog.

"How would you like a nice diamond ring?" said Father.

"I want a dog," I said.

"Well, he will have to stay where he belongs," said Father. "I won't have a dog running around the house."

So he erected a doghouse. It was built of selected lumber, it would have held a pony easily, it was shingled, painted, had a fancy hinged door, and a small window.

Timmie was eight weeks old when he came, no bigger than a large bunny. He spent one night in his mansion yelling his head off. I wept bitterly inside the house, and the next day Timmie moved to the cellar. He never set paw in the doghouse again. From the cellar it was only a short haul to my bedroom.

When I went East to school, Timmie slept at the foot of Father's bed. Somebody got the doghouse to raise chickens in.

A few years later, I was married and living in Virginia, and Father was going off on a Sabbatical, so Timmie was shipped to me.

Father took Timmie to a train that left home at two-thirty in the morning so the trip would be easier for him.

POMP AND CIRCUMSTANCE

He built a crate for the journey. The express men were a little dazed when Father and the crate arrived and Timmie got down from the front seat. The crate was even more stately than the doghouse, and it weighed as much as a piano even without Timmie in it. It was furnished with a number of feeding dishes, water bowls, bags of food, rugs.

On the top was painted in large red letters, "Timmie is a good dog. Be kind to him!"

When, after fourteen years, Timmie died, Father dug him a grave under a hawthorn bush at the bottom of the hill and buried him like a gentleman. On his grave flowers bloomed, and for all I know, a hardy perennial may blossom there today.

No dog after Timmie was suffered to come in the house, and Father dealt a well-placed kick to any who came too near. It was as if he resented any dog being alive when Timmie was dead.

Mamma gave up all her outside activities when Timmie was sick and sat with him, and it was quite a time before she went back to her regular routine.

Father didn't think much of her clubs, but Mamma loved them. Her favorite was the Dickens Club which met weekly. It had gone on for years and it went on indefinitely. A group of women met and read Dickens aloud as they sewed. They read their way steadily through *Oliver Twist, Tale of Two Cities, Nicholas Nickleby,* and finally when they got through down to *Martin Chuzzlewit,* they began all over again with the *Pickwick Papers.* Father said it was an awful waste of time, but Mamma said Dickens was a fine writer and they loved him.

They had tea and little sandwiches and colored icing on

tiny cakes afterward, and the only resignation ever offered for the Dickens Club was involuntary. A member could die.

Aside from the Clio Club, the Town and Gown, and the Dickens Club, there were social evenings. The faculty members had dinner together and played charades. Mamma never could guess a charade, but she loved the dressing up and acting.

Eventually, playing cards came into favor. This was like the sea breaking through a small hole in the dike. First there was the evening of rook, then whist became respectable, and finally five hundred swept in with a great tide.

And in the end, bridge was played.

Naturally nobody played any games on Sunday, but Saturday night dinners with bridge became common, and bridge luncheons were instituted with prizes.

As soon as Father became persuaded that it was all right to play, he loved it. At first he pretended he played only to please Mamma, and he reached for the deck with a sheepish look and a shy grin. But all the time as he dealt, his blue eyes would shine, and his cheeks grew pink.

Mamma was naturally a good player, although she couldn't count well enough to keep score and didn't care for games. She played quietly along, never really caring whether she won or not.

But Father had to win.

This had nothing to do with any tangible reward, for playing for money was unheard of, and the prizes were negligible.

Father's method of playing was simple. He just bid higher than anyone else, no matter what the bid was or what cards he held.

This meant that he always played the hand, which was more fun than being dummy. If anyone else ever did manage to play a hand, Father got restless and kept telling his partner what he should have played.

He couldn't bear to lose, and with his private system of bidding, the scores against him could be terrific. This he laid to the fault of the cards or to some opponent who had "pushed him up."

"I just had to bid seven no trump," he would say to Mamma, "to get the bid!"

His favorite bid was no trump. He didn't like the feeling that someone might sneak in and trump a good trick, so he bid no-trump even with a blank suit.

As books on bridge began to percolate our province, some of the faculty grew quite expert at a reasoned game.

But Father never counted his hand. "Nonsense," he said, "all you have to do is hold the high cards and play them out."

He had such a flawless memory and such quickness, he might, with a different temperament, have made a fine player. But as long as he paid no attention to the most basic laws, he was a menace.

He maddened some partners and frightened others. And the worst of all was that he nearly always got the best cards in the deck. Whereas Mamma, who was willing to play by rule, almost never had more then one face card in her hand.

If she tried to get Father to follow the conventions, he pushed her off. "I play for fun," he said.

"But it's more fun for everybody if you play right," said Mamma.

Father shook his head. "I play for fun," he said.

At the height of the bridge playing fever, there was a big tournament party at the Country Club. The college people, the townspeople, the young and old were there.

I was out of town, but I heard about it.

Father won the grand prize.

"But I don't see how he could have!" I gasped, "with all those experts."

"Well," said the friend who told me, "it was really pretty awful. Nobody could tell what he was bidding on or what any of his bids meant and it threw them off so. All his partners got confused. But so did all the people who played against him. And you know he always has the high cards." She laughed. "You can imagine how they felt when the final scores were added up and your father had the highest of anybody!"

Father was not at all surprised. It was perfectly simple. He held the high cards and took the bid and played the cards out, beginning with the ace and going right on down. What he held in his hand was a secret until he began to play, for informational bids were not in his field.

"We had a good time," he said. "I had good cards most of the time. Sometimes I had to go pretty high to get the bid, but I got it."

When it came time for Father's Sabbatical leave, he went to Europe. The next time he whisked through South America, including crossing the Andes. Mamma hoped that would satisfy him, for traveling with him was always so strenuous.

In the first place, he would never tip anybody. He did not believe in it and thought it a waste of money. He paid the price for his lodging, meals and travel, and that was all he did pay. So Mamma went all over Europe slightly in the rear of his progress nervously hiding tips under napkins. She had to be careful and quick, for if Father turned around and saw her, he would dash back and whip up the money and pocket it.

"But you have to tip," she would say weakly.

"No, you don't," said Father. "I have no patience with employers underpaying the help and expecting me to make it up."

I have been over-tipping all my life, due to the effect of Father's habit, and I always put the tip in the middle of the table, so the waiter will be sure to see it right away.

Secondly, Father always went in any place that had a KEEP OUT sign posted. He didn't like to feel restricted. This made Mamma very nervous, and she always expected he would be clapped in jail sometime.

Thirdly, he always looked like a tramp when he barged into the most elegant hotel. He was frequently told there was no room available. Then he would tell the staff who he was and where he came from and where he was going, and he might give them a brief talk on the wonders of their scenery or geological formations. Presently he and Mamma would be installed in a good room with bath. And the staff just adored him—until he dashed off at the end leaving not a penny behind for anyone.

Fourthly, he traveled so fast that it was all Mamma could do to get a night's sleep in any one location.

Then, too, Mamma was not at her best on the ocean. She got miserably seasick at the slightest ripple and stayed that way. Father dosed her liberally with Mothersills, lemon juice, coffee, bromides, and anything else he had in his medicine box, and it only made her worse.

"If you'd just come up on deck," he said, "and get the wonderful ocean breeze."

"Leave me alone. Go away," Mamma always moaned.

Father was all over the ship, down with the firemen, sneaking up to the bridge. He felt simply wonderful, and the more the ship rolled, the better he liked it.

The only time he ever yearned for land was the trip when they were caught in a hurricane in mid-ocean. The ship rolled half over at every wave, water flooded the decks, china crashed in the dining room, and things looked very bad.

Around midnight, Father got up and shook Mamma's arm.

"Get up! Get up and get dressed!" he said.

He was pulling on his trousers as he spoke. "Hurry up," he said. "She's going down."

Mamma moaned faintly, "Then why should I get up?"

Father stopped and stared at her, his shirt in his hands. "Well, my gracious," he said, "if you're going to drown, you want to drown with your clothes on, don't you?"

Mamma didn't care.

She hoped that was the last voyage. But the next thing she knew, Father was studying maps again.

"I guess we'll go to Africa," he said. "We've never been there."

The next thing Mamma knew, Father became the flying professor. The minute plane travel became possible, Father was all for it. Mamma said if he wanted to risk his life, he could risk it alone.

Father flew to Canada where the plane had to land on a frozen lake, and that was wonderful. He flew over the desert, and he flew East. He got so he would only travel by car or in a plane, and if he could have his own plane, life would be wonderful.

Mamma said nobody would be safe in the air if Father got to whirling around in it.

His cruising speed in the car was seventy-five miles an hour, and when he had to slow down to fifty for a town, he always apologized, saying, "I better go slow, I'll get arrested."

Once the car broke down during a trip, and Father had it repaired and then took the garage man for a spin to test the motor. The garage man came back pale and shaken. "Never again," he said, "will I ride with that man! He ought to be in with Barney Oldfield."

Father might be off on a jaunt looking at a mine in the desert, and he would give his examinations at the last possible moment. But as the year turned, he was always at home and ready for Commencement.

For Commencement Day at the college was the windup of the long year. May Day festivities were over, the Senior Play was done with, the tennis finals won and lost. Father paid no attention to these, but Commencement was part of his job.

He was prepared to do his duty at Commencement.

The weather always turned hot that particular week, the sky was polished blue flame, the elms brilliantly green, the lawns soft and deep.

It was a lovely time, the end of the school year, the girls and boys drifted arm in arm on the river paths now sweet with white clover. The band practised in the gymnasium with windows open, and the sound of the Alma Mater and *Pomp and Circumstance* floated out pleasantly in the still mellow air.

The girls wore light summery dresses, bright in the sun and shimmery in the moonlight. They looked young and innocent as flowers. The boys had their hair cut and wore clean shirts and pressed flannels.

In the town gardens, the lilacs hung in purple clusters and the first peonies were out, shell pink and ivory. There was a sweet smell of summer in the air, and a dreamy amethyst haze over the hills beyond the river.

The chapel doors were wide on Commencement morning. The seniors, awkwardly pushing their caps around, assembled on the stone steps. The faculty procession formed by Science Hall and marched under the canopy of elms toward the chapel.

Led by the president, the professors marched in twos down the long walk, their academic robes blowing a little in the light air. They wore long heavy hoods folded back to show the deep and glowing colors of their college degrees, the scarlet, the lake blue, the white, the raw gold. The mortar boards rested firmly on bald heads, curly heads, grey heads. The long tassels swung.

Father's hood was deep with blue velvet bands, and I always thought how fortunate this was, because blue was his color.

Mamma and I would stand by the steps watching, her

delicate summer dress blowing, my pink tissue gingham wilting in the sun.

Slowly and solemnly the academic procession advanced, mounted the wide steps, disappeared in the shadowy chapel.

Gone now the quirks and queerness of the professors, gone the bickering voices raised in faculty meetings. With the ancient cloak of learning folded down upon them, the men walked with proud dignity.

They were not, now, husbands and fathers. They were men dedicated to the life of the mind and the spirit.

As they moved slowly up the steps, this was made visible.

Father walked with his head high, his eyes straight ahead, his restless feet for once slowed and his tread measured. Under his swinging tassel, his curly hair was bright, and the stitched point of his cap made a dark peak on his high forehead.

His mouth was calm, a little dreamy, he was a scholar and a teacher, and in his eyes the color of unknown worlds of glory shone with a clear flame.

As Father moved past us, I cried in my handkerchief and Mamma had a strange deep look.

The great sound of the organ came out, *Pomp and Circumstance* echoed in the golden air.

Father never smiled at us, he was a dedicated man as he entered the chapel and made his way to the seat on the rostrum.

Mamma and I always got home first, because the procession wound its way back to Science Hall before disbanding.

We took off our garden flowery hats and got the gloves put away, and then Father would come billowing down the street at a fast canter, his hood over his arm, his mortar board askew.

His face was hot and red, his curls damp as he came up the steps and flung himself in the hall.

"Thought that man would talk forever," he panted, wrestling with the heavy silk cord under his arms. "Nearly boiled up there. Lunch ready ?"

"In a minute," Mamma said.

"Well, let's eat and pack up and get off for the cottage. No use waiting around here in all this heat until tomorrow."

Commencement was over.

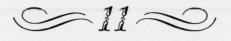

Full Circle

FATHER NEVER APPROVED FOR A MINUTE OF MY LEAVING home. He wanted me right under his own roof, it upset him to have a change in the household. When I went away to school, he would drive me to the station with his face set and white. Mamma would be bravely cheerful, to make the parting as easy as possible, but he got more and more upset as the time for the train to come grew nearer.

We always got to the station hours before time to go, and Father would rush in and out of the baggage room checking on my trunks and suitcases. He would run down the wooden platform looking toward the Junction. He would get in the car and back it around in a different place.

He would dart into the waiting room and make a phone call.

"Hang on to your purse," he always said. "Don't let anyone snatch it. Watch out for your ticket. Be careful about the taxis across Chicago."

"Yes, Papa," I said.

I always felt perfectly dreadful. In fact, I felt I was probably going to die. I looked my last at everything. The little mustard brown station, the stuffy waiting room with the round black stove in it, the baggage wagon, the traveling salesmen ready to hawk their wares in the big town—these were sharp in my mind.

Looking back down the street, I could see the trees flaming with brilliance, the houses, the still green lawns. The ugly porches, the cupolas, the bay windows, the gingerbread decor—these looked lovely to me. The streets of home were beautiful, I thought.

The train rocked down the track from the Junction and the great sickness invaded my stomach.

Then I got angry enough to feel my temples pound. I didn't want to go East for an education, I never had. I wanted to stay with my own friends, in my own town, at our own college. This was all Father's doing, sending me across the country.

He had picked the college, he had chosen my course of studies, he had even picked out my brown suitcase.

Well, I hope you're satisfied, I thought savagely.

Father's mouth was tight, and as the train slowed and stopped, he rushed to me and grabbed me in his arms and his eyes were filled with tears.

"Be a good girl," he muttered hoarsely, and flung himself away.

"Have all the fun you can," Mamma said, kissing me without tears. Her hands were trembling as she drew back.

Clearly and distinctly I see them on the bare wooden platform, Mamma waving her handkerchief, the sun on her brown velour suit, her feathered hat, Father blowing his nose. His head was bare and his curly hair rumpled. His trousers sagged at the knees, he was hot from emotion and his shirt was unbuttoned at the collar.

This was a brief moment, even as the train gathered

speed I could see Father drag Mamma away and I knew he was saying, "Come on now, let's get started. We can't stand here all day!"

In the course of time, after I married, I really moved away. Father didn't approve of this either, although summers we still spent together, as well as Christmas and sometimes Easter.

But he felt better when I moved back to New England, only a hundred miles from the part of Massachusetts where he was born.

On occasion, I could drive up and see the aunts and uncles, and when he came East, he could go home by way of my place, and whisk in briefly.

The old homestead was sold by now, the stately pillars unpainted, the porch steps sagging, the yard grown up with crab grass. Only the big rosy hydrangea trees were the same, lining up across the lawn in a mass of bloom. The sign for tourists hung by the porch.

Times were hard, the days of plenty were gone, and the pleasant woman who owned the place was put to it to keep the old mansion going.

Father and I went through it once, a sorry pilgrimage. Gone the grand piano, the Navajo rugs, the bearskin, the golden oak furniture. The house seemed empty and silent. The medicine closet was still there, a remembered island, and the sun still shone through the green stained-glass windows. Father stood in the doorway of Grandfather's study. The desk was gone and the great armchair and the steel engravings. A sewing machine was under the window.

He stood silent, his hands opening and closing. Then he

said, "This was my father's room." And he bolted back down the hall.

The aunts lived in their own smaller houses now, the uncles were scattered in neighboring towns. We usually gathered at Aunt Lida's, which was central.

One particular family reunion was planned because my cousin Richard was flying back from the West. He had been away since childhood, had grown up, married and had children way off across the country. Nobody approved of this, but the family was gathering to greet the returned prodigal. Richard had done very well as a physician, but still he ought to live nearer home.

Father had come East to locate water for a paper mill. I had picked Richard up at the airport and we drove together to our aunt's house. I had on a new grey suit and a hat with pink and blue flowers on it.

Father was standing on the steps as we drove up and he ran down to the car, looked me over, sniffed audibly and said, "Well, I didn't know you! Thought it was some movie actress!"

I had not seen him for some months, and I looked at him anxiously. He was seventy-seven that spring.

"How are you, Papa?" I asked as we went up the walk.

"I'm a little tired," he said, "I've been climbing mountains all day. Had to cut my way part of the time."

"Oh, Papa," I said.

"I found the water all right," he said. "I'm getting a good flow for them. But I slipped and fell in a brook and tore my pants."

"You better get a good rest now," said Richard.

"I'm driving back to Wisconsin tomorrow," said Father. "I have to hurry. I have another job there Monday."

Two aunts were sitting on the front porch in the high green rocking chairs. They had their hats and coats on.

"Where have you been?" they called together. "You were supposed to be here an hour ago!"

"Get right back in the car," said Aunt Fanny. "We'll just get in with you and we can drive right to the cemetery."

Father said, "The light's going. I want to get some pictures first."

"But if it gets dark we can't see the names on the headstones," said Aunt Lida.

"Stay right there," said Father. "It won't take long." He flew into the house and came out with his equipment. Richard looked nervous.

Father set up his tripod and got the camera on it, flung a black cloth over his head.

"Now Richard you stand a little farther over. No, not that far. Fanny, you get in the middle. No, Lida better get in the middle. Now take off that movie actress hat. Don't scowl."

It was the same as it had always been. We stood in one spot, were shifted to another. Had the tree for a background, had the porch, had my car. Father rearranged our positions. My hat went back on, came off.

By the time we were glassy-eyed and rigor mortis had set in our grinning faces, Father suddenly without warning snapped the shutter and then said fiercely, "There, you spoiled everything, Gladys! Why can't you stand still! How can I get a decent picture when you jiggle around so?"

Then we hurried to the cemetery. Father wouldn't go. He said he had things to do. The two aunts were plump and a little crippled with the family arthritis, but their faces were fresh and young, their eyes shining and clear. They loved going to the cemetery, they bounced into the car with their rich curly hair flying, their gloved hands fluttering.

"I don't know what's the matter with Rufus," Fanny said. "He never seems to enjoy the cemetery."

When we drew up again at the house, Father was standing at the curb.

"What in the world have you been doing all this time?" he demanded.

"We were just going over the lot," said Fanny. "Father's stone holds up well, but that white marble stone of Majel's was a terrible mistake. I told you that you would regret it. You can hardly read the name now. In fifty years it will be gone."

"I don't see what difference it makes," I said perversely. "Who's going to care in years to come?"

There was a horrid moment of silence, then Lida turned to me with dignity. "It's historical," she said.

"Walter's stone will last forever," said Father. "You can't wear out that granite."

I took his arm and squeezed it. Yes, polished granite for Walter, I thought, but pure white delicate and soft marble for your darling Majel.

"We went over to the other cemetery, too," said Lida. "I wanted Richard to see Ralph's stone. He might like that for his mother."

Richard looked pale. Father explained. "Ralph couldn't

be buried in our own cemetery," he said. "He wasn't related except by marriage." He added firmly, "Every single one buried in our cemetery is a relative."

"Yes," said Fanny, "and there were seventy-five living relatives at the last funeral. And when I think that your poor mother is the only one not laid to rest there—" she dabbed at her eyes.

"I don't know what she was thinking of," said Father. "I don't believe in cremation. I would have told her so."

"A terrible thing," said Fanny. "And whatever made her do it? Not even an urn so we could have a service."

"It was Mother's last wish," said Richard.

"But there's a place for her," said Father, "right next to mine. Faces east too." He added, "She was always notional and poetic. But the idea of having the ashes scattered from the top of Pike's Peak!"

"We told Richard he could put up a stone anyway and we would have a service still," said Lida. "The new minister preaches such lovely funerals."

"Granite," said Father. "I'll pick it out for you. A nice red granite, it has a fine color. Bright and cheerful."

I thought of the cemetery as we had walked over the soft spongy turf. The last pencil of light marked out the names of my buried ancestors, the pale gold handwriting of the sun was on the stones. Dark and somber stood the pines, bright leaves fell softly from the maples. The awful serenity of the dead lay upon it. You too shall fall and lie here, the leaves said.

But Father and the aunts were bustling about the house, and the rest of the relatives began to drive up, and the smell of roast beef was an assertion of living.

Presently we sat down to the big roast, mashed potatoes, great bowls of brown gravy, new peas, creamed corn, tomato salad, jelly, pickles, olives, celery, hot rolls, ice cream on apple pie, and coffee. Topped off with nuts and chocolate candy, the family finished the meal.

One of the small nephews had a scratched finger.

"Now I know what to do for that," said Aunt Fanny. "You soak it in epsom salts. Draws the poison out."

"I'm all right," he said.

"There was a boy died here just last week," she said. "He cut his foot on a nail. Buried three days later."

The boy stopped eating. "It hurts awful."

"Milk poultice is the thing," said Lida, "sweet milk and bread."

"You bind a piece of bacon rind on it," said Father. "No trouble at all. Stepped on a nail last week and tied up the foot with bacon rind, no bother at all."

"Mrs. Elder has grippe," said a cousin.

"Well, I could tell her what to do," said Fanny. "That wild cherry bark tonic will cure it."

"Palm oil is better," contradicted Lida. "I had such a cold I thought I couldn't sing last Sunday in church, and I took half a bottle of palm oil and it cleared it right up. Tastes good too."

Father took a third piece of pie and a little more ice cream. "The best thing for grippe was that Collygog in the brown bottle that Mamma used to give us. Cures anything. Don't know why they stopped making it. But if you feel a cold coming on, you can break it up fast with rhinitis and quinine and aconite for the fever."

"Quinine makes my head ring," said Uncle Ned. "Can't abide the stuff."

"I cured my arthritis," said Aunt Fanny proudly. "Last year my knee was so bad I could hardly walk. I just could get out of bed in the morning. Couldn't even go hunting." She poured more coffee and stirred in three spoonfuls of sugar. "It pained awful. Then this year I got sick and tired of it so when deer season came around I cut me a good cane off one of the trees by the back door, and went hunting anyway. And I fell down crossing a brook, fell flat on my face, twisted my leg back up under me. And when I could get up after awhile, I was all right."

"You exercised it," said Father. "Plenty of exercise is what you needed." He said, "I stiffen up now and then, and I go out and chop some wood and limber up all right."

"A dozen lemons a day in a glass of water is the best thing for arthritis," said Aunt Lida.

"You'll take the enamel right off your teeth," predicted Father.

I looked at Richard. "Do you have many arthritis patients?"

"Why, that's so, Richard is a doctor," said Aunt Fanny. "I suppose you may know something about ailments. You might as well take a look at my knee as long as you are here and it won't cost anything."

She jumped up from the table and ushered him out with her. Nobody paid any attention, they went on happily prescribing sure cures for all the ills of the flesh. When they came back in, Aunt Fanny was saying, "and you just try Dr. Burrough's Expectorant and see what happens."

I asked Richard privately about her knee.

He grinned and shook his head. "Amazing," he said. "I guess she knocked off some calcium deposits, but I never had a chance to tell her. She was curing me."

The family crowded into the parlor. The walls of the room seemed to lean out a little. The older generation settled themselves in the best chairs, the young ones perched on wooden ones. The aunts and uncles looked so hearty, so indelibly young, and so much alike. They were all short, stocky, plump with fresh complexions, crisp curling hair, definite imperative voices.

They were now in their sixties and seventies, but I thought the younger generation looked older and seemed bloodless and pale beside them. Vitality blew like a spring wind from them.

The various wives and husbands, sitting at the edge of the circle, seemed rather vague and shadowy figures. No doubt they had personalities of their own, but you wouldn't notice it now.

"But nobody ever notices us," one of the cousin's wives echoed my thought, as I visited with her. "They are so awfully alive."

Father was getting hot in the crowded room, so he began opening up the windows. Someone complained, and Father said, "Fresh air won't hurt you. It's suffocating in here."

Aunt Fanny got out her knitting bag and began to work on her blue fascinator. Father picked up the bag and poked around and brought out her duck call which she always carried with her, and blew it loudly to try it out.

"There's a can of mosquito paste in there too," she said,

purling busily. "You try it next time you go on one of those climbs."

"I never pay any attention to mosquitoes," said Father. "If you move fast enough they don't bother you."

He took her best fishing reel from the bag and inspected it carefully.

"Fishing is too slow," he said. "Hunting is the best."

Aunt Fanny tucked the reel and the duck call back in the bag, and began to cast off for the shoulder, needles clicking.

"You should have seen the buck I got this year," she said. "Biggest I ever saw."

Richard had moved over and was staring at her. I suspect he would have had Aunt Fanny on a light diet and a quiet regime for some time had she been his patient.

"Where did you get him?" asked Father.

She laughed, her eyes shining with excitement. "I just went where he was," she said. "I went along the path to where I figured he would cross, and I found me a nice solid stump to sit on while I waited for him." She looked at me. "I am a comfortable hunter," she explained. "I was there from around six till noon and then I got hungry so I laid my rifle down beside me, got out my thermos and poured my tea and unwrapped my chicken sandwiches. I always carry plenty of tea."

Father said, "I hope you had the safety on your gun."

"Just as I got the cup full," said Aunt Fanny, "I looked up and there," she pointed a knitting needle dramatically, "there he came! The biggest buck I ever saw! Coming right at me! I put down my tea without a sound," she whispered, "and slowly—slowly reached for my rifle," she bent to the parlor carpet and slowly grasped an imaginary gun.

"And then bang—bang—bang—" cried Aunt Fanny, firing point blank at Father.

"Right between the eyes," she finished, happily. "He just sank."

"Good shot," said Father. He looked proud of her. "Then what?"

"I just sat there," she said, "and waited. I couldn't drag him myself. I figured after awhile the men would miss me and come looking. Around dark, they did."

"It must have been awfully tiring," I said.

"Oh, I had my tea then," said Aunt Fanny, "and my lunch. And I kept waving my red hat now and then, you never can tell when some crazy hunter may shoot you."

Richard was looking at her with awe. "And did the men get any?"

"They never even had a chance to shoot," she said complacently. "I told them, you just have to go where the deer are, that's all."

I went out to the kitchen for a drink of water. Uncle Ned's voice followed me.

"And he tried to arrest me," he was saying, "and I just leaned out of the car and said to him, 'Young man,' I said, 'I have been driving a car since before you were born, and you can't teach me how to drive!'"

"What was the matter?" Father's voice sounded impatient. He thought little of the law himself.

"Not a thing. Passed a red light, but they don't need a light there anyway. I've been driving that river road for years and nobody ever got hit there yet."

FULL CIRCLE

"I don't believe in red lights," said Father, "I don't pay any attention to them as a rule. I can tell if a car is coming without any light blinking at me."

I put down the glass and rested my eyes a moment looking at the cool dark outside. Then I walked back to the parlor.

"So old Mr. Bailey came over and he had just killed a woodchuck," Aunt Fanny was saying. Everyone else was talking too, including Father, but that never bothered the family.

"He had already buried it, but I said I never tasted woodchuck but I don't know why we don't try. Go dig it up," said Aunt Fanny, "and I'll cook it. It wasn't buried very long."

Father said, "Was it good?"

"Well, I cooked it with onion and made nice gravy, but the truth is, it was kind of tough." She sighed. "I wouldn't go to shoot woodchucks for eating."

Father said, "You can take rattlesnake and make a meal, but I wouldn't pay much for it. They call it a delicacy. I'd rather take my rattlesnake at the end of a gun, blow its head off and bury it."

"Suppose you miss," said a timid in-law.

Father laughed heartily. "I never miss," he said.

All the aunts and uncles laughed too. The idea of one of them missing a shot!

"You can always pin him down with a forked stick by the back of the neck," Father said generously, "if you haven't got your gun."

"Can't we have some music?" I asked.

They were all out of practice, the whole seven of them. They said they couldn't possibly perform, and meanwhile

[245]

they surged toward the piano so vigorously that the tall vase of plumed grass shook and almost toppled off.

Aunt Lida sat down to play, settling her comfortable bulk firmly on the stool. She struck a few chords.

"Needs tuning," said Father at once.

Uncle Ned and Father began to go through the piles of music, rejecting everything that they already knew, and looking for something untried. Finally they found something, and then they all wanted it sung in a different key. Lida played it in two keys, and they settled on a third.

Night had deepened by now, and the street lamps were lit. They shone with a pale glow through the stiffly starched lace curtains. Fanny turned on the silk-shaded lamp, and the long fringe swayed from her vigorous hand.

The lamplight fell on the portraits of Grandmother and Grandfather in their heavy carved gilt frames.

Below them, their children stood around the piano, the aunts well corseted, the uncles with tight-buttoned vests and stiff collars. The voices rose, the piano sounded deep and full.

Suddenly I saw them, no longer greying and plump, but young and slim, their voices clear with youth, their eyes bright with dreams. Father was smiling, and his tenor rose clear and pure to the top notes.

The sister beside him let her full contralto notes sweep out and beyond her, the clear light soprano rang like a flute. Aunt Lida's fingers, just a little knotted with arthritis, slid along the keys rapidly, gathered up the chords and flung them out triumphantly.

This could not last, but for the moment they were reaching the top notes, making the parlor vibrate with music as brave as youth.

"You flatted that high note," said Fanny to Father.

"That's the wrong key," he retorted. "I never flatted in my life and I shan't begin now."

"You took it too fast, Lida," said Ned, "slow up in the middle of page two."

"Don't slow up too much," warned Father.

I looked at them, the family, and it seemed to me there was some meaning here that almost escaped the mind. I had to find it. This was more than a collection of strong individual personalities, it was a reflection of part of America that we may not see again.

I thought of the first ancestor, back there in 1632, setting his firm unfrightened foot on the new and terrible terrain.

It was his crest, and he was perfectly confident that he was virtuous and noble. And if the goodly man cheated the Indians, it was always for their own good, or for the glory of God. If he persecuted the witches, he was saving their souls or defending the innocent wretches they were casting spells upon. Sin was his mortal enemy, compromise a word he never knew.

Something lackadaisical has come into us these later days, I thought. We have lost the rugged strength, the stubborn will. The sight of these, the last of the Puritans, standing there gave me an uneasy sense of weakness in my own generation.

Not one of them, I said to myself, would abandon their principles for expediency. If the time came for Communism to sweep the world, Father would face a firing squad still shouting, God bless the Republican Party.

But as for me and the cousins—I wondered, and I looked around for the cousin most kin to me. Rob had been sitting in the corner and now he got up and wandered out to smoke his pipe, not being allowed to smoke in the house, of course.

I followed him out, smiling a little to see how he moved with the same rolling walk Father had. Blue eyes and fair hair and compact strong body, even the hands with strong squarish palms identified him as his father's son, as family.

He moved to his car and picked up his guitar and sat on the steps and drew a strong thumb over the strings. I sat down beside him.

"Too hot in there," he said.

"Rob," I said, "would we stand by our principles at any cost?"

"You mean like the rest?"

"You know what I mean."

"Sure." He plucked a minor chord, "Sure. Well, in little things we'd be all right. But suppose it meant losing the house and the job and not having enough to feed our children—well, maybe I'd sell out. I don't know. To save things." He swept the strings mournfully.

"The thing is they believe in themselves so wonderfully," I said. "They have no doubts."

"Do you remember when we thought God was that picture of Grandfather?" asked Rob.

"And family prayers."

"I wonder what we're passing on to our own children," said Rob. He began to play *To Each His Own* very softly. "I don't know. I guess we never can know."

A little lost dog began to bark down the street. The moon was standing over the rooftops.

"Someday you ought to write about the folks," said Rob. "In a few years, nobody will remember this kind of family. America is changing so fast, and with the atomic age here, who knows where we will end?"

"Children, come right back in the house!" Aunt Fanny was in the doorway, "You'll catch cold out in that night air!"

We looked at each other and laughed, and went back in.

Father was singing alone now, *La Golondrina,* in Spanish. He was pleased to think he still remembered the foreign tongue, after all these years. His voice was filled with feeling.

His strong profile was outlined against the patterned lace at the window behind him. His head was lifted a little, and he gestured with one hand.

Perhaps he was remembering the mountains of Mexico and the days of hard riding and the danger at night and the silver spurs and the brave sombrero. Or little faraway patios with fountains playing and small dark children staring at the young gringo.

I, too, remembered him thin and hard and young. I wished I could talk to him, break down the barriers, go back with him.

He was wearing a new light grey suit with a pin stripe of blue, and the trousers already bagged at the knee. His hair was silvery and as thick a bush of curls as one was apt to see. His face was burned from the day of mountain climbing, his eyes blue as deep water, and his mouth softer than usual because he was singing.

How familiar every detail was to me, even to those old fashioned high black shoes and the grey wool socks. And yet could I ever know him, had anyone ever known him at all?

The last note died away. Father turned abruptly from the piano.

"Wasn't there some apple pie left?" he asked. "I didn't have much appetite at dinner."

Uncle Ned said he hadn't eaten much either. Nor had Aunt Fanny. Nobody had done more than nibble, it appeared, although those mountains of food must have gone somewhere!

The aunts bustled out to the kitchen and there was much cutting of cold roast, slicing of cake, brewing of fresh coffee. They still drank coffee all day long and slept like tops all night, so they had no patience with the few in-laws who timidly refused a cup.

Richard went out with me to lock up the car since it was getting late. "How can they eat again?" he said.

"They're hungry," I said.

"What do you think I ought to do about that stone?"

"Get it," I said, running up a window. "They'll never forgive you if you don't. Let Papa get it, he'd love picking out the best granite. And he's sure to get it for less too."

"I can't understand them," he said.

"Well, if you do move away from New England," I said, "the least you can do is to get back one way or another, dead or alive."

"They are rather overpowering," he said, "but I'm glad I came. I didn't know how rootless I was."

"Nobody related to this family can ever be rootless," I said.

Frost was in the air, and a feeling of change. I shivered suddenly and pulled my sweater up around my throat. The sky looked cold and the street dark and empty. The house was as bright as a ship bearing down on us.

As we opened the door, the voices surged around us. They were all too busy talking to hear us.

Talking about us.

"They both seem to me to look a little weak," said Aunt Fanny.

"They don't get enough exercise," said Father definitely. "That's the trouble with them."

Around midnight, the family began to scatter. The aunts and uncles collected their own children and rummaged for wraps and got into their cars and drove away. Richard and I were sent over to Rob's for the night and admonished by Father to get right to bed and not sit up any later.

"I have to get off early," he said, "I've got to be back in Wisconsin right away." He said, "If you want to see me, you'll have to be here by seven-thirty."

"Papa, why can't you take your time?" I said.

"My gracious, I've been here two days," he said.

So the next morning I got up early to say good-bye to Father. I had caught a cold and was feeling feverish and shaky. My knee was aching like sixty. In short, the family reunion had worn me out.

My cousin gave me some aspirin, which never agrees with me, and I swallowed a hasty breakfast with one eye on the clock. It seemed very natural to be hurrying on account of not keeping Father waiting a minute. So much of my life had been spent trying to keep up with him.

I left the car and walked around the block to the aunt's house, and Father was out on the steps looking up at the sky to see whether it would rain.

"That hat," he said. "Where did you get it? It looks just like a movie actress."

I thought perhaps this was a compliment and not an insult. But I took it off and hung it by the elastic on my arm.

We went in for a round of coffee. Father was packed, his bags in the hall, his coat flung over a chair. He had already had eggs and bacon and pancakes and maple syrup and coffee, and Aunt Lida was washing up the dishes. It was seven forty-five.

Father was as brisk and fresh as a newly opened marigold. His hair was still damp from being whacked down with a wet brush, and the curls stood up all over his head in little feathery curves.

He wore a clean bright blue shirt and his new good suit, a little more mussed than it was the evening before. One button had given up and popped from the shirt.

We had the coffee and then Father got restless.

"It's getting late," he said. "I want to make five hundred miles today. I've got to get started."

"You ought not to take that long trip alone," I couldn't help saying, "and so fast. I wish you had come on the train."

"I don't like the train," he said. "It's a nuisance."

"Well," I said, "well, Papa."

We went out and stood on the steps and I looked at him. A sudden mist blinded his eyes and he took out his handkerchief and blew his nose. "Must be catching cold, too," he said.

Then he threw his arms around me and squeezed me in that breathless bear hug, and he kissed me good-bye.

"Now you be a good girl," he said.

And these were the last words he was ever to speak to me.